Niagara

Niagara

a novel

by

Michel Butor *translated*

by

Elinor S. Miller

Henry Regnery Company

Chicago

Dedicated to travelers in the West

I

Introduction

Busy readers will take the short track by skipping all the parentheses and all the preludes.

More leisurely readers will take the long track without skipping anything.

But all the readers of this book will enjoy following the directions for the use of the parentheses and exploring little by little the eight intermediate tracks in order to hear how, within this liquid monument, a change in lighting will cause new forms and aspects to appear.

Two voices in the center, that of the Announcer, loud; that of the Reader, fairly loud.

Seven volume settings or positions will be available, designated as follows:

> very soft,
> soft,
> fairly soft,
> not too loud,
> fairly loud,
> loud,
> very loud.

The directions for volume must be followed even if one can afford only a single-channel production.

A bell peals once, very loud.

ANNOUNCER **During the year 1791, Viscount François-René de Chateaubriand perhaps came to contemplate the cataract of Niagara. In 1797 he published a famous description of it in his "Historical, Political and Moral Essay on Ancient and Modern Revolutions, Considered in Their Relationships to the French Revolution":**

> *It is formed by the Niagara River which springs* READER
> *from Lake Erie and empties into Lake Ontario. At*
> *about nine miles from the latter lake are the falls;*
> *their vertical height may be some two hundred feet.*
> *But what helps to make them so violent is that, from*
> *Lake Erie all the way to the cataract, the river flows*
> *steadily downward along a steep incline, a distance*
> *of almost six leagues, with the result that at the very*
> *edge of the cascade it is less a river than an impetu-*
> *ous sea whose hundred thousand torrents rush to-*
> *ward the gaping mouth of a chasm.*

(the pitch of the voice rises slightly)

> *The cataract divides into two branches and curves*
> *into a horseshoe of about half a mile around.*

(a little more)

> *Between the two falls juts out an enormous rock,*

> *hollow underneath, which hangs with all its pines*
> *over the chaos of the waves.*

(in a dignified tone)

> *The mass of the river, which hurls itself southward,*
> *bulges and becomes rounded like a vast cylinder at*
> *the point of leaving the shore, then unrolls in a sheet*
> *of snow and glistens in the sun with all the colors*
> *of the prism; the one falling toward the north de-*
> *scends in fearful darkness like a pillar of water*
> *from the flood.*

(slower)

> *Countless rainbows curve and cross above the abyss,*
> *whose dreadful booming can be heard for ·sixty*
> *miles around.*

(slow and noble)

> *The waters, striking the shaken rock, splash back up*
> *in whirlwinds of foam which, rising above the*
> *trees, resemble the thick smoke of a vast forest fire.*

(slow, very dignified)

> *Gigantic, immeasurable rocks, cut into phantom*
> *forms, adorn the sublime scene; wild walnut trees,*
> *reddish and scaly with sap-wood, grow, stunted, on*
> *these fossil skeletons.*

(very slow)

> *No living animal is to be seen nearby,*

It goes without saying that the spectacle has much changed.

> *except eagles,*

Much changed; François-René de Chateaubriand already knew it when he took up the account of his travels again in his "Memoirs from Beyond the Grave":

(very natural)

> *Today wide highways lead to the cataract; there are*
> *inns on the American shore, and, on the British*

shore, mills and factories below the gulf.

The inns have become two cities.

(resuming his sentence as if from very far away)

> *except eagles who, soaring above the cataract where they come to seek their prey, are*

And from all points of the United States, by express-ways and byroads, in jeeps or Cadillacs, dragging behind them ladles and saucepans, the newlyweds converge here.

(returning)

> *swept along by air currents and driven down in spirals to the depths of the abyss.*

(whispered)

> *Some striped badger*

Thus, all along the access roads, whether one comes via Rochester or Buffalo, at intervals among factories and fertilized fields, hotels and motels are spaced out, some brand-new, others tumbled down, with pictures of cascades.

(like a tempter)

> *hanging by his long tail*

(more and more insinuating)

> *at the very end of a low branch*

(a little irony is mixed in with the insinuation)

> *tries to catch*

(a little more irony)

> *the remains*

(fading away)

> *of the drowned bodies*

(slower)

> *of the elks*

(distinctly enunciating the words)

    and of the bears

(normal speed, almost inaudible, except the word "flings" flung out)

    that the backwash flings ashore.

II

The Couples

Ten tracks: A B C D E F G H I J

Tracks A B C : Skip the parentheses.

Tracks D E F: Read "Memories and Tulips," omitting Abel's and Betty's lines.

Tracks G H I J : Read everything.

in the center:

loud:

ANNOUNCER

at left:

fairly loud:

CHARLES AND DIANA: old married couple

at right:

not too loud:

ABEL and BETTY: "just-marrieds"

in the center:

fairly soft:

READER

The voices of Announcer and Reader are always in the center.

When the left channel is completely closed, Charles and Diana can still be heard, but softly.

When the right channel is completely closed, Abel and Betty can still be heard, but very softly.

By adjusting the balance of his speakers, the listener can give more or less emphasis to one side or the other.

Little Prelude for nine o'clock

Between the first eleven notes of the Westminster carillon, soft, something like a catalogue of sound effects can
be heard, very soft but distinct:

> in the center:

>> — *automobile starting up* —
>> — *scrap iron being dragged* —
>> — *horn honking* —
>> — *brake screeching* —
>> — *car door being opened* —
>> — *booming* —
>> — *crowd noise* —
>> — *sighing* —
>> — *flag flapping* —
>> — *car door being slammed* —
>> — *leaves rustling* —

The ringing of bells is always heard in the center, but
the sounds printed at left or right will be altogether to
the left or right, respectively, so that the listener, adjusting the balance of his speakers, may emphasize or even
silence one side or the other.

The possibility of variation is therefore twofold: for the
broadcast, the producer will have chosen one of ten
tracks; at the receiving end, the listener will be able to
move around within the interior of the transmitted ar-
chitecture.

Since the mobility of reading is much greater than that of any listening, you may imagine, with book in hand, all kinds of combinations.

— booming —
— car doors being opened —
— brakes screeching —

soft, with the last notes of the carillon as nine o'clock
strikes, very soft, among the following lines:

> *— horns honking —*
> *— scrap iron being dragged —*
> *— automobiles starting up —*

ANNOUNCER   **Here we are in the street of the falls.**

On each side are restaurants,

dime stores,

movies,

and souvenir shops,

                 I . . .   ABEL

displaying flags with waterfalls,

                     . . . love you.   ABEL

                 I . . .   BETTY

plates with waterfalls,

                     . . . love you.   BETTY

shirts with waterfalls,

> Your eyes. ABEL

ashtrays with waterfalls,

> Your eyes. BETTY

medallions with waterfalls made of butterfly wings,

> The tears of your eyes. ABEL

table napkins with waterfalls,

> All the pearls of your eyes. BETTY

> Your lips. ABEL

postcards with waterfalls, slides with waterfalls, miniature toilets with waterfalls, pillows with waterfalls, tapestries with waterfalls, buttons with waterfalls,

> My heart leaped in my breast when BETTY
> you were watching me put on my
> lipstick this morning.

bedlamps with waterfalls,

> And it was a new face that you ABEL
> found in your mirror this morning.

little naked porcelain women whose breasts come off to make salt and pepper shakers,

> I saw in my eyes your eyes laughing. BETTY

ties with waterfalls,

> And why did you need lipstick to ABEL
> seduce me this morning? What I
> wanted was just your lips all pure
> and raw.

decanters with waterfalls,

> I wanted to dress up my lips in our BETTY
> honor this morning.

hairbrushes with waterfalls.

> Decorate them with flowers. ABEL

All the petals were ripped off by   BETTY
your laughter,

scattered   ABEL

It is formed,   READER

by your breath,   BETTY

it,

all around your real lips,   ABEL

by the river,

like a crown of little flames that   BETTY
burn me.

is formed,

**The street of the falls leads to Prospect Park, the park
with the view.**

Niagara,

**The expressways are crossed via elegant concrete
bridges.**

by the river,

One can see the metal-and-glass elevator tower,

which springs from Lake Erie,

**and farther away, on the Canadian shore, the big
hotels,**

Niagara which springs from

**with the sign for the wax museum, "Madame Tus-
saud's," clearly visible,**

and empties

**and the carillon tower which crowns the International
Rainbow Bridge,**

from Lake Erie

where the hour is striking:

— leaves rustling —

> *—car doors being slammed—*
> *—flags flapping—*

fairly soft, as ten o'clock strikes, soft, among the following lines:
—sighs—
—crowd noises—
—booming—

> *into the Ontario,*

The hour passes.

> *about nine miles,*

The day passes.

> *about nine miles from the latter lake,*

The month passes.

> *from the latter lake,*

Time slips by into time.

> *are the falls, their height,*

**Automobiles go toward Canada, and young couples
on foot lean on the parapet between the two flags,**

> *the falls are vertical,*

**the flag of the United States with its fifty stars embroi-
dered in silver on the blue field,**

> *some two hundred feet may be their vertical height,*

seven red stripes,

> *but what helps perhaps to make them so violent,*

six white stripes,

> *some two hundred feet, is that . . .*

the flag of Canada, red,

> *but what, from Lake Erie, helps, all the way to the
> cataract, to make them so violent . . .*

with the Union Jack in the upper left quadrant,

> *the river flows steadily . . .*

and the shield.

> *is that, from Lake Erie, flowing downward all the way to the cataract,*

Among the crowd of young couples, here are some obviously older:

> *along a steep incline, the river flows, for a distance of almost six leagues, steadily downward*

CHARLES   Everything has changed.

> *with the result that at the very edge of the cascade, along a steep incline, it is less a river, for a distance of almost six leagues,*

DIANA   We have changed.

> *than a sea, with the result that at the very edge of the cascade, it is less a river than a sea*

Rainbow Bridge, built in 1940–41, replaces Honeymoon Bridge, which collapsed under ice pressure, January 27, 1938, at 4:13 in the afternoon.

> *whose hundred thousand torrents rush toward the gaping mouth of a chasm, the cataract whose hundred thousand torrents*

CHARLES   After the flood.

> *divide and rush in two branches toward the gaping mouth of a chasm,*

At the end of Rainbow Bridge is the customs office.

> *and the cataract curves into a horseshoe, divides into two branches and curves,*

DIANA   After thirty years we have come back.

> *of about half a mile around,*

CHARLES   That enormous tower that looks like a castle of water used not to be there.

If you are a citizen of the United States or of Canada, you will have no difficulty;

DIANA   That little belfry with the carillon wasn't there.

into a horseshoe between the two falls,

CHARLES Or that elevator with its iron-and-glass cage on the other bank.

of about half a mile around.

DIANA Was that wax museum, "Madame Tussaud's," there?

If you are from another country, you may sometimes have to submit to lengthy interrogation.

We have crossed the border. ABEL

Juts out

Here we are in another country. BETTY

an enormous rock

Queen Victoria Park runs along the gorge on the Canadian side.

between the two falls,

This is what they call another ABEL country.

hollow,

In the middle, the open-air theater, in the interior of which we find: ornamental rocks,

CHARLES I saw only you.

juts out underneath,

DIANA Were these flowers here?

an enormous rock that juts out

ponds,

They dress the same way we do. BETTY

hangs

CHARLES It's the beginning of tulip time.

with all its pines,

DIANA And the cars were all different.

terraces,

But the Canadian dollar is worth a   ABEL
little less than ours.

hollow,

But they don't walk just the same   BETTY
way we do.

over the chaos of the waves

CHARLES   Can you read the name written on the label?

paths,

DIANA   In front of this scarlet patch?

bushes,

underneath.

flowerbeds,

CHARLES   "Big City!"

and the amphitheater with its tiers of seats.

DIANA   Remember?

First Parenthesis of MAY

(Memories and Tulips)

ANNOUNCER   **The hour passes,**

                           And this red on the whiteness!   ABEL

slips by into the day.

                           Why do you want to know the   BETTY
                           names?

The day

CHARLES   I bought you some.

slips by

DIANA   A few years ago.

into the month.

                           Don't you want to know the names?   ABEL

On May 15 begins

                           But we don't have a garden!   BETTY

the tulip festival.

CHARLES   It wasn't so long ago.

                           Not yet.   ABEL

DIANA   When we came here.

BETTY. Not right away.

CHARLES. Ah, we didn't have a garden!

ABEL. Not for years.

DIANA. We didn't even have a house.

CHARLES. We slept in a room at one of your uncles'.

DIANA. There was no kitchen; I had to use that reeking oil stove, and I didn't know one single thing about cooking, and I would hear you coming up that wooden staircase outside, all worried, and you would say to me, "I haven't found anything; everything costs so much too much."

BETTY. Not for years.

CHARLES. And then we unearthed that one-room apartment in the Bronx.

ABEL. Oh, I don't intend to buy one.

DIANA. And we crossed over the river. In the kitchen in Queens, there was an oven.

BETTY. Oh, we couldn't buy one.

CHARLES. We had a car then; we moved by ourselves.

ABEL. If you read me the names, you will take on their colors.

DIANA. And then a Negro came to live in our house.

BETTY. "Furnace."

CHARLES. He had two darling little girls.

ABEL. Furnace.

DIANA. Oh, I had nothing against Negroes, and especially not against those Negroes!

BETTY. Scarlet.

CHARLES. Certainly, we have nothing against Negroes.

ABEL. Frosted.

DIANA. But it was unpleasant in the long run.

BETTY   Yellow heart.

CHARLES   And then the children . . .

ABEL   Black stamens.

DIANA   When they used to come home from school and their friends would see them turning into a Negro street.

BETTY   "Big City."

CHARLES   There wasn't any way to bring them home in the car every day.

ABEL   Big City.

DIANA   There wasn't any way to explain it to them either.

BETTY   What city could be like a flower?

CHARLES   For us it didn't matter.

ABEL   Like this scarlet flower.

DIANA   Not too much.

BETTY   devoured by yellow flames . . .

CHARLES   But to inflict on them . . .

ABEL   What city roaring in flames,

DIANA   And then . . .

CHARLES   The smell . . .

ABEL   shimmering,

READER   *The mass of the river*

DIANA   The day when Cecilia told me . . .

BETTY   shimmering,

CHARLES   What did Cecilia tell you?

ABEL   shimmering,

DIANA   Of course I must have told you. I was terribly upset. One day—she was just coming in from school—she said to me, "Mom, what is that smell?" I asked her, "What smell?" But naturally I had understood all right. Then she burst into tears. It was one of those silly girls, one of her friends who was already wearing lipstick—I don't remember her name anymore—who had yelled out to her, I don't know why—some argument—"But really, when you go home, don't you find that smell annoying?"

which hangs,

        carpeted in flowers.   BETTY

CHARLES Do try not to talk so loud.

        "Ibis."   ABEL

DIANA And the terrible thing is that I just stood there speechless. If I had known what to answer her right that moment, it might have been possible perhaps . . . But the minutes fell like drops of water through a crack in the ceiling.

        Pink flushed with white.   BETTY

which hurls itself southward

CHARLES And when I came home that evening, you said to me: Please, please.

        Double-flowered.   ABEL

DIANA There was nothing to be done.

        "Electra."   BETTY

CHARLES No matter what they say, there is nothing to be done about the smell, and I did try!

over the chaos of the waves,

        Carmine with luminous purplish ABEL
blue.

DIANA And you who wanted to read; you said that you would have liked to read sometimes.

        These are like peonies.   BETTY

CHARLES And then your uncle in St. Louis died.

the mass of the river bulges,

        "Golden Dawn."   ABEL

DIANA You took me away.

                                    Bright yellow flushed with bronze   BETTY
                                    and cerise.

CHARLES   We went over the Brooklyn Bridge.

                                    The outside is red like a "Stop"   ABEL
                                    sign.

DIANA   That tunnel under the Hudson.

                                    The inside is a somber red like the   BETTY
                                    poison, curare.

            and becomes rounded like a vast cylinder

CHARLES   There was a plot of grass in front.

                                    The base of the petals is yellow like   ABEL
                                    a "Slow" sign.

DIANA   I remember; we had a package of ten bulbs, but four
        never bloomed.

                                    And becomes green near the stem   BETTY
                                    like a "Go."

            which hurls itself

CHARLES   And we looked in the catalogues for the names of the
          flowers.

                                    The light's turning green. We can   ABEL
                                    cross.

DIANA   There was one called "Big City."

Second Parenthesis of MAY

(The Flowers' Invasion)

at the point of leaving the shore,   READER

    Here are some in pure white called   BETTY
    "Kansas."

ANNOUNCER   **On May 15 opens**

    Darling . . .   ABEL

also the festival

    Here are some violet ones trimmed   BETTY
    with silver called "Arabian Mys-
    tery."

bulges southward,

of lilacs.

then unrolls

    I love you.   ABEL

and becomes rounded in a sheet,

    I love you.   BETTY

like a vast cylinder of snow,

    The "Fair Angel" tulip, bright sul-   ABEL
    phur delicately striped with scarlet.

at the point of leaving the shore,

> The "Golden Measure" tulip, yel- BETTY
> low gold very delicately edged with
> scarlet with your stamens of saffron.

and glistens,

> Pure white lilacs. ABEL

then unrolls in the sun in a sheet

> Reddish purple lilacs. BETTY

with all the colors of the snow and glistens in the sun

> "Smiling Queen" tulip, pink trim- ABEL
> med with silvery pink, a white base.

of the prism with all the colors.

> The "Sunny Boy" tulip, luminous BETTY
> orange striped with a brighter
> ground of egg yellow, stamens of
> bright yellow.

The one falling from the prism toward the north,

> Lavender pink lilac. ABEL

The iris festival begins on May 24.

> Wine-colored lilac. BETTY

*the one descending, falls in a fearful darkness
toward the north,*

> Iris with pure white petals on sepals ABEL
> ridged in spring yellow with the
> delicacy of an orchid.

as a pillar of water from the flood descends.

The rhododendron festival

> A very big light golden brown iris BETTY
> with sepals shaded with lilac.

Countless rainbows

begins in the last days of May,

A big cobalt lilac tinted with mauve.   ABEL

in a fearful darkness curve,

when the tulip festival is ending.

Very big lilac of vivid gillyflower   BETTY
red.

like a pillar,

Insurpassable lilac-colored tulip.   ABEL

and cross above the abyss whose dreadful booming
of water

Deep scarlet tulip with a bright vio-   BETTY
let ground frosted like a lily.

can be heard for sixty miles from the flood,

NNOUNCER **At the end of Queen Victoria Park, one finds the tunnel elevator.**

> *around the rainbows.* READER

>> Rhododendron ABEL

> *The waves,*

Ticket office. Souvenir counters:

> *countless,*

>> red . . . BETTY

> *striking the rock,*

hairbrushes with waterfalls,

> *curve and cross,*

>> White with blackish red spots. ABEL

> *shaken, splash back up above the abyss*

decanters with waterfalls,

> *in whirlwinds whose dreadful booming of foam*

>> Brilliant soft pink spotted with BETTY
>> yellow.

> *can be heard for sixty miles around,*

ties with waterfalls,

> *which,*

>> Huge lilac with white flowers in   ABEL
>> bunches.

> *striking the shaken rock,*

**little naked porcelain women whose breasts come off
to make salt and pepper shakers,**

> *rising, splash back up*

>> Very beautiful deep red lilac.   BETTY

> *above the trees in whirlwinds,*

bedlamps with waterfalls,

> *resemble the thick smoke that rises above a vast
> forest fire.*

>> Lavender blue lilac.   ABEL

> *Immeasurable rocks resemble the thick smoke,
> gigantic, cut into the form of a vast forest fire of
> phantoms;*

buttons with waterfalls,

> *rocks adorn the immeasurable and sublime scene,
> gigantic walnut trees cut into phantom forms,*

>> Lavender pink lilac.   BETTY

> *wild, adorn the scene with a sublime reddish sap-
> wood, and scaly walnut trees grow, stunted, wild,
> on these skeletons of a fossil reddish sap-wood.*

tapestries with waterfalls,

> *No living animal is to be seen nearby, and, except
> for the scaly eagles who grow, stunted, soaring over
> these skeletons above the cataract where they come
> to seek their fossil prey, swept along by air currents,
> one does not see . . .*

>> Iris   ABEL

*And driven down in spirals to the depths of the
abyss, no living animal . . .*

pillows with waterfalls,

*And, except eagles, the badgers who hang by their
tails, soaring, flexible above the cataract . . .*

chrome yellow tinged with orange   BETTY
in the center,

*At the end of a low branch where they come to seek,
to seize, their prey, are swept along by the current
in the abyss of air and driven down . . .*

slides with waterfalls.

*Carcasses broken in spirals in the depths of the
abyss of elks and bears and badgers.*

soft pink reminiscent of the tones   ABEL
of the flamingo.

The hour passes,

III

The Negroes

Tracks A B: Skip the parentheses.

Tracks C D: Read "The Roses."

Tracks E F: Read "The Roses" and "The Glance," but omit Arthur's and Bertha's lines.

Tracks G H: Read "The Roses" and "The Glance."

Tracks I J: Read everything.

in the center:

loud:

ANNOUNCER

at left:

fairly loud:

ELIAS and FANNY: Negro gardeners

not too loud:

CHRIS and DELIA: old married couple (cross right after "The Dew")

in the center:

fairly soft:

READER

at right:

soft:

ARTHUR and BERTHA: "just-mar-rieds"

If the right-hand channel is completely closed, Chris and Delia can still be heard when they are at right, but very softly; Arthur and Bertha disappear.

Do not attempt to give an accent to the Negroes.

Do not attempt to put any lyricism into the "readings" of the flowers; only a discreet erotic contagion.

Little Prelude for eleven o'clock

In time with the first ten notes of the Westminster carillon, fairly soft, can be heard:

  in the center:

    at right:

  soft:

    very soft:

  —*branches snapping*—
  —*drop of water*—
  —*elevator machinery*—

        —*automobile starting up*—

  —*waterproof clothing rubbing*—
  —*newsboy*—
  —*laughter*—
  —*trickling*—

        —*scrap iron being dragged*—

  —*footsteps on damp rock*—
  —*footsteps on damp wood*—
  —*buzzing*—

Some of these noises are continuous: automobile, rubbing, trickling, machinery; some can become so. Thus
they can not only appear between speeches but also
persist behind them more soft.

When Arthur and Bertha speak, one of the continuous sounds of the left-hand channel resumes the volume with which it was introduced in order to fill the silences that would be produced if the right-hand channel were completely closed. The result is that in some cases, with the normal setting, these sounds will cover their speeches; the listener can then amuse himself by removing this covering of sound effects in order to discover them intact underneath.

— waterproof clothing rubbing —
— elevator machinery —
— drops of water —

fairly soft, with the last notes of the carillon as eleven
o'clock strikes, soft

> *— branches snapping —*
> *— scrap iron being dragged —*
> *— automobiles starting up —*

ANNOUNCER   **The day passes,**

> What would you rather do?   ARTHUR

> We can wait.   BERTHA

postcards with waterfalls,

> *They are formed by the river, and badgers hang by*   READER
> *their tails.*

**table napkins, medallions with waterfalls made of but-
terfly wings . . .**

> *Flexible Niagara which springs at the end of a*
> *branch from low Lake Erie and empties into the*
> *Ontario at about nine miles*

the month passes . . .

CHRIS You want to go back into the tunnel?

DELIA Of course we must go back into the tunnel.

> *to catch in the abyss of the latter lake the broken carcasses of the elks and of the bears.*

ashtrays, shirts with waterfalls,

> *Are found the falls of the eagles, their height . . .*

plates, flags with waterfalls.

> *Swept away by the vertical air current, descend perhaps in spirals of about two hundred feet to the depths of the chasm.*

Well, do you want to go into the   ARTHUR
tunnel?

Of course we have to go into the   BERTHA
tunnel!

> *But what helps to make them so violent is that the rocks*

In the same building, to remind us carefully that we are in a monarchy,

> *from immeasurable Lake Erie, and all the way to the gigantic cataract,*

the reproduction in glass and brass of the crown jewels,

> *the river flows steadily . . .*

treasure of the Tower of London.

> *cut into phantom forms . . .*

The elevator is cut into the rock.

> *downward along a steep incline . . .*

**Down there,
each visitor receives a pair of boots and an orange raincoat.**

> *adorn the scene.*

They get there through a tunnel behind the great wall
of headlong water.

For a distance of six sublime leagues.

Then the guide takes a pebble in his hand

With the result that at the very edge of the cascade,

and throws it at the dark, raging liquid windowpane,

it is less a wild river than an impetuous sea

which opens up for a split second,
to let a flash of garish light streak through.

First Parenthesis of JUNE

(The Dew)

ANNOUNCER **At the beginning of June is the end of the lilacs.**

of reddish and scaly sap-wood, READER

The wind carrying away the white ARTHUR
petals.

whose hundred thousand torrents

The earth sprinkled with these little BERTHA
blue shells.

grow,

Blue with orange papillae. ARTHUR

rush,

Enormous with pink winey petals BERTHA
and sepals of velvety garnet red; it's
called "Chief."

stunted on these skeletons toward the gaping mouth

Iris! ARTHUR

CHRIS Faded.

O my iris! BERTHA

DELIA Crumpled.

Ivory and strawberry pink. ARTHUR

CHRIS   Wrinkled.

                Heliotrope.   BERTHA

DELIA   Dried.

        fossils of a chasm.

The rhododendrons are already fading.

CHRIS   Rotted.

DELIA   Fallen.

        The cataract,

                A white swarm with blackish red   ARTHUR
                spots.

                I feel a little like a stranger.   BERTHA

        striking the rock,

                Don't you want to go in and rest?   ARTHUR

                No hurry.   BERTHA

        divides, shaken,

                It's nice out.   ARTHUR

                Fresh sunshine . . .   BERTHA

        into two branches, splashes back up

                With this drizzle,   ARTHUR

                this dew   BERTHA

        and curves

                iridescent   ARTHUR

        in whirlwinds

                on all the blades of grass,   BERTHA

                on all the pistils.   ARTHUR

        into a horseshoe of foam

                I want to be alone with you.   BERTHA

                It's the noise.   ARTHUR

It's the crowd, too. BERTHA

of about half a mile around,

June 10 begins the peony festival.

which, rising between the two falls

Deep garnet red. ARTHUR

above the trees,

Distinguished. BERTHA

Nonchalant. ARTHUR

juts out,

Newlyweds of that very day, who hesitate, who are nervous about the coming night,

resembling the thick smoke of a vast forest fire.

Set off by the golden bouquet of the BERTHA
stamens.

An enormous rock, countless rainbows,

newlyweds of the day before who have already spent their wedding night in one of the hotels, and who look at each other in wonder,

hollow underneath curve and cross

O my incomparable silk! ARTHUR

over the abyss whose dreadful booming can be heard for sixty miles around, which . . .

I love you. BERTHA

—footsteps on damp rock—
—trickling—
—laughter—

not too loud, as noon strikes, fairly soft

—newsboys—
—waterproof clothing rubbing—
—elevator machinery—

ANNOUNCER   **old married couples who had come to the falls and who have tried to find the same room again,**

        The one which　　　　　　　　　READER

pass an old married couple

        hangs, falls,

who had not been able to come then, thirty years ago,

        with all its pines descends,

and who are here seeking the fountain of youth,

        over the chaos of the waves, in a fearful darkness,

who have saved penny by penny for years,

        the mass of the river,

who did without a new refrigerator,

like a pillar of water from the flood which hurls it-
self southward,

in order to be able to come see the peonies,

ELIAS Soft

FANNY Flesh-colored,

Did you see those Negroes?   CHRIS

ELIAS Brilliant velvety amaranth with silvery flecks.

Why are you looking at those Ne- DELIA
groes? They are just Negroes.

Second Parenthesis of JUNE

(The Roses)

FANNY My fine, my beautiful purplish red tinged with garnet shaded with maroon.

The mass of the river READER

I was wondering if . . . CHRIS

ANNOUNCER **in order to be able to come see the last of the irises.**

But you know perfectly well that all DELIA
Negroes look alike!

bulges and becomes rounded like a vast cylinder,

Porcelain blue. ARTHUR

They would certainly have recog- CHRIS
nized us.

They would certainly have spoken DELIA
to us.

which hurls itself southward,

Flax blue. BERTHA

ELIAS Copper yellow.

at the point of leaving the shore

Yellow throat. ARTHUR

bulges,

FANNY   Tawny sepals.

Why are you looking at them like   CHRIS
that?

ELIAS   Bronze.

I just have the feeling that they are   DELIA
following us!

FANNY   Dark, purplish, velvety.

No, really, you're imagining things;   CHRIS
look at those two instead.

Throat with cream flecks.   BERTHA

then unrolls in a sheet of snow and glistens,

Those others have turned into an-   DELIA
other path.

Changing from yellow gold to straw   ARTHUR
yellow.

June 15 begins the rose festival.

and becomes rounded in the sun

Double-flowered.   BERTHA

Feathered.   ARTHUR

Well formed.   BERTHA

like a vast cylinder

Light.   ARTHUR

Delicate and warm.   BERTHA

with all the colors,

Salmon.   ARTHUR

Madder red.   BERTHA

at the point of leaving the shore of the prism,

Brick red.   ARTHUR

Brilliant.	BERTHA

then unrolls.

Luminous.	ARTHUR
Full.	DELIA
Dazzling.	BERTHA
Wide.	ARTHUR
With fringed petals.	CHRIS
Shaped like great anemones.	BERTHA
Deliciously fragrant.	DELIA
Geranium red.	ARTHUR
Salmon cream.	CHRIS

ELIAS   Sprung from a hardy crimson bud.

Turkey red.	BERTHA
Abundantly flushed with pink.	DELIA

FANNY   Lusterless.

Erect.	ARTHUR
Carmine on the edge of the petals.	CHRIS

ELIAS   Shaded with dark garnet.

Strong.	BERTHA
Scarcely tinted toward their bases.	DELIA

FANNY   Veined.

Branching out.	ARTHUR
One last fragrant peony.	CHRIS

ELIAS   Striped.

Beautiful foliage.	BERTHA
Fragrant amaranth.	DELIA

FANNY   Orange shaded with lavender changing to lavender pink, very erect stem.

Splendid. ARTHUR

Sulphured. CHRIS

ELIAS And the last iris of pure yellow gold.

Velvety. BERTHA

Silky fragrant. DELIA

FANNY Smoked yellow, plum red sepals, velvety bordered with cream.

Cochineal carmine. ARTHUR

Floribunda. CHRIS

ELIAS Delicately perfumed.

With white undersides. BERTHA

Moss-roses. DELIA

FANNY On very shapely stems.

The one falling toward the north descends

Bluish lilac-colored changing to lav- ARTHUR
ender mauve.

in a sheet of snow in a fearful darkness, glistens in the sun

ELIAS Thorns.

Blood red clouded with scarlet. BERTHA

FANNY Red fruits.

Bengal fire. CHRIS

ELIAS One day a drop of blood on your mauve skin.

Bushy. DELIA

FANNY One day a whole stained-glass window of savage blood in the yellowish white of your eyes of bronze.

Fragrant. ARTHUR

ELIAS And the petals of your purplish pink lips velvety with black so perfumed, plucked by a ray of sunlight in your bosses' basement.

		BERTHA

Fragrant.   BERTHA

FANNY   The translucent red thorns stationed all along the cuttings you planted at your bosses' place.

like a pillar with all the colors of water of the prism,

Like those at your parents' home.   CHRIS

ELIAS   Your fingernails painted like petals fallen to earth.

Like those you brought them the   DELIA
first time you came to their house.

FANNY   Your hands covered with earth which you washed in order to caress me, but which smelled of soap and earth with the scent of roses above the manure, your nails still all framed in earth like young sprouts.

—scrap iron being dragged—
—automobiles starting up—
—buzzing—

fairly loud, as one o'clock strikes, not too loud

> *—footsteps on damp wood—*
> *—footsteps on damp rock—*
> *—trickling—*

> *the cataract of the flood*   READER

ANNOUNCER **Couples married thirty years,**

> *divides into two branches and curves into countless*
> *rainbows,*

couples married the day before,

> *a horseshoe,*

trembling couples married this morning,

> *curve and cross on horseback over the abyss of*
> *about half a mile around*

white or black,

> *whose dreadful booming can be heard,*

**here they are passing through customs again in their
cars, their buses, or on foot.**

Third Parenthesis of JUNE

(The Glance)

with the result that at the very edge of the cascade,	READER
Farewell, delicate,	ARTHUR
Roses with peony petals.	CHRIS
for sixty miles,	
soft,	BERTHA
Peonies with iris petals.	DELIA
beautiful,	ARTHUR

*it is less an impetuous river whose hundred thou-
sand torrents around*

ELIAS Farewell, my bronze leaves whom I have so watched
over.

Iris with tulip petals.	CHRIS
very beautiful,	BERTHA

*rush toward the gaping mouth of a chasm, the
waves,*

red	ARTHUR

FANNY Their green blood on your rough fingers.

*but what helps to make them so violent, striking
the shaken rock.*

ELIAS   My buds of milky coral,

*is that from Lake Erie all the way to the cataract
the river splashes back up in whirlwinds of foam,*

FANNY   And the bees buzzing in their tea bush in the midst of
walls of skin.

flows steadily downward along a steep incline,

ELIAS   Look!

*which rising above the trees for a distance of al-
most six leagues*

glazed,   ARTHUR

resembles the thick smoke of a vast forest fire;

FANNY   When you no longer have on your coveralls with the
pruning shears sticking out of the pocket . . .

brilliant.   BERTHA

*rocks immeasurable and gigantic of perhaps about
two hundred feet*

ELIAS   Listen!

FANNY   What did they say when you told them?

cut into phantom forms adorn the scene.

ELIAS   I lied to them.

FANNY   They were going on a trip, too.

*At about nine miles from the latter lake are the
sublime falls.*

ELIAS   Don't turn around!

FANNY   The folds of the flag flapping softly, rubbing in the
sticky pollen.

> *They are formed by eagles swept along by the*
> *Niagara River.*

ELIAS The concert of automobiles.

FANNY They are passing us in a car.

> *The current which springs from the lake of air, Erie,*

ELIAS But what did you see?

FANNY I really thought it was the boss's children.

> *descends in spirals to the depths of the chasm,*

ELIAS Because they got married?

FANNY One of the two was supposed to get married.

> *and the badgers hang*

ELIAS Which one?

FANNY I don't remember.

> *by their flexible tails*

ELIAS But which did you see?

FANNY I don't know now which one I saw.

> *at the end of a low branch,*

ELIAS Did you really see him?

FANNY I didn't look.

               to catch in the abyss   READER

ELIAS   Young people pass by behind us,

FANNY   in both directions.

               the broken carcasses

ELIAS   Young people pass by behind us,

FANNY   white,

ELIAS   pink.

               of the elks

FANNY   Their red blood flows under their skin.

ELIAS   They hold each other's pale smooth hands.

               and of the bears,

FANNY   They pass by.

ELIAS   They are going to the Canadian shore.

               and empties into the Ontario.

IV

The Bridal Veil

Track A: Skip the parentheses.

Track B C D: Read "Hesitations Before Entering."

Track E G: Read "Sarcasm" and "Hesitations Before Entering."

Tracks F H: Read "Sarcasm," "Hesitations Before Entering" and "Story of the Shirt," omitting Andrew's and Bettina's lines.

Tracks I J: Read everything.

in the center:

loud:

ANNOUNCER

at left:

fairly loud:

GERTRUDE: old madam

HECTOR: gigolo

not too loud:

ELMER AND FLOSSIE: Negro gardeners

in the center:

fairly soft:

READER

at right:

soft:

CLEM and DOROTHY: old married couple

very soft:

ANDREW and BETTINA: "just-marrieds"

The characters whose names begin with the same letter can be played by the same actors, but it would be better to use at least two couples in alternation.

The couples speak to each other in isolation, Andrew with Bettina, Clem with Dorothy, etc., without regard for what the others are saying. They must be rehearsed first separately.

If the left-hand channel is closed, Gertrude and Hector can still be heard, but softly; Elmer and Flossie, but very softly. If the right-hand channel is closed, neither Clem and Dorothy nor Andrew and Bettina can be heard anymore.

Little Prelude for two o'clock

In time with the first nine notes of the Westminster carillon, not too loud, can be heard:

        in the center:

at left:

                at right:

        fairly soft:

soft:

           very soft:

    —machine-gun spray of water—
    —jingling—

           —automobile starting up—

    —foghorn—
    —brass band—

           —waterproof clothing rubbing—

    —wind howling—
    —rain—

—booming—

    —creaking—
    —dance music—

           —footsteps on damp wood—

    —thunder—

When Andrew and Bettina speak, one of the left-hand sounds resumes its initial volume; when Clem and Dorothy speak, one of the left-hand sounds is heard at one volume setting below the original; so they will be hidden less often than the "just-marrieds" and will reveal themselves before they do.

First Parenthesis of JULY

(Sarcasm)

FLOSSIE   They're going toward the United States shore.

ELMER   They're trembling.

ANNOUNCER   **The hour passes.**

FLOSSIE   They feel tears rising.

ELMER   They don't feel.

The day passes.

FLOSSIE   They don't know.

ELMER   But you know how to feel.

They are formed,   READER

FLOSSIE   But you know how to feel things out.

ELMER   But you know how to figure things out.

they are formed,

FLOSSIE   But you know how to thrash things out.

ELMER   What a flower I've found, what springtime in this fruit which is wrinkling, how many seeds!

FLOSSIE   Gently.

The month passes.

ELMER   It wasn't them.

FLOSSIE   I don't know.

they are formed by the river,

ELMER   And the other one, when she used to come to the shed at the back of the garden when she was twelve or thirteen.

FLOSSIE   When he used to come to my kitchen.

by the Niagara River which springs,

ELMER   She used to watch me wash my hands.

FLOSSIE   He used to open the door so softly.

And here, among the ordinary couples, coming down the paths of the American park,

ELMER   Once, I used to take her, pick her up, kiss her.

FLOSSIE   One day, it was as if a curtain were closed, a door slammed shut.

by the river

ELMER   They didn't recognize us anymore.

FLOSSIE   They wouldn't have recognized us anymore.

passing a first bridge,

ELMER   But you would have recognized them, you would.

FLOSSIE   They don't know.

ELMER   They don't know anymore.

Niagara which springs from the lake,

FLOSSIE   There is something in them which would have been able to.

ELMER   There is something in them which still might be able to.

FLOSSIE   They don't know how to look after themselves anymore.

crossing the Isle of Green, or, more exactly, Green Island, from the name of a late director of this park, formerly named the Isle of the Bath, because a souvenir shop had a little swimming pool in its basement,

ELMER   They no longer know how to look at each other.

FLOSSIE   No longer know how to look at us.

from Lake Erie and empties,

ELMER   There is something in them which is still looking.

FLOSSIE   There is something in them which is stifled.

passing over a second bridge,

ELMER   They saw us, but they probably avoided us.

FLOSSIE   We will disturb their wedding night.

Niagara,

ELMER   There is something in them which will be watching out for

FLOSSIE   a smell . . .

turning right on Goat Island (a certain John Stedman, at the end of the eighteenth century, had a farm on the shore, and transported to the island his flock of goats in the fall of 1778; all perished of cold in the winter, except the billygoat),

Erie and empties

—jingling—
—machine-gun sprays of water—
—booming—

not too loud, with the last notes of the carillon as two
o'clock strikes, fairly soft

> *—footsteps on damp wood—*
> *—waterproof clothing rubbing—*
> *—automobiles starting up—*

> *into the Ontario, at about nine miles from the lat-*   READER
> *ter lake,*

NOUNCER   **a lady much made up and manicured,**

> *which springs from the lake,*

no longer very young,

> *into the Ontario,*

her fingers covered with rings,

> *are the falls,*

with a young man who could be her son,

ERTRUDE   It is ugly, I agree with you, it is ugly, it is ridiculous, all
these fools gaping at that flowing water . . .

HECTOR   But I told you perfectly clearly that I didn't want to come here.

reaches the elevator which leads to the cave of the winds.

Second Parenthesis of JULY

(Hesitations Before Entering)

and empties   READER

;ERTRUDE   Yes, I know that, my pet; don't get mad, pet.

HECTOR   You asked me to drive you here; I have driven you.

into the Ontario

;ERTRUDE   It is because I wanted to see you here.

HECTOR   And now you don't like it anymore.

at about nine miles from the latter lake.

;ERTRUDE   I like it enormously, my pet; why are you nervous that
          way? I understand why you are nervous that way; you
          are a child, you could almost be my son, I have a son as
          big as you, but he is so ugly and silly . . . Only, in the
          midst of all this crowd and all this noise . . .

Shall we go?   ANDREW

At about nine miles from the latter lake are the falls.

HECTOR   Well, you're the one who's jumpy now.

Let's go.   BETTINA

Their vertical height

;ERTRUDE   How could I be jumpy when I am near you, when I see you so fresh and so deliciously ill at ease. Then, you really want to go down with me into this cave of the winds, it doesn't bore you too much to be in the company of a woman who is somewhat mature and looks so much as if she were your mother?

Shall we go back there?   CLEM

may be

HECTOR   Don't keep saying that all the time, you grate on my nerves.

Let's go back there.   DOROTHY

of about two hundred feet . . .

GERTRUDE   I will be a good mother to you; you will never have had a mother like me, you'll see. No, if you please, don't tell me about your mother . . .

are the falls.

HECTOR   But you know very well that . . .

Their height

ELMER   What's going on?

FLOSSIE   We'll find out.

—rain—
—wind howling—
—brass bands—

fairly loud, as three o'clock strikes, not too loud

—foghorns—
—jingling—
—machine-gun sprays of water—

GERTRUDE   When I came here with my husband . . .

HECTOR   Because you came here with your husband?

vertical perhaps   READER

NNOUNCER   **From the elevator exit a hilarious dripping troop of yellow-gold capes pours forth.**

of about two hundred feet, but

GERTRUDE   I had begged him, I was very young then, I knew nothing about his life, I was younger even than you are now, and I was beautiful then, I was very beautiful, I know it, you can't imagine . . .

HECTOR   You know very well . . .

what helps to make them so violent,

They go into another building very close by.

their height,

GERTRUDE   Oh! I've done everything to preserve some vestiges, and
it wasn't so difficult to create an illusion for you, you are
so new to all that! And he, he found everything frightful, and it's true, all this is frightful, I see it now, and it
is completely ridiculous to want to go down into the cave
of the winds.

HECTOR   Be nice. Since we are here now, it would be fun for me;
it would be fun for me to go down there with you.

but what helps to make them . . .

They pay.

*is that, from Lake Erie all the way to the very vio-
lent vertical cataract,*

GERTRUDE   As for me, it amuses me enormously to go down there
with you, and I am so happy that you want to go down
there, because he, he refused me, because I asked him
to stay a day longer for that, and for all the rest, and he
burst out laughing, and that day . . . and it was for
that that I wanted absolutely to wait, my darling, until
we got to this place, which is frightful, my darling, I
realize that it is frightful, but it wasn't possible, we
couldn't stop in any old motel, you understand that, my
darling, tell me that you understand, I wanted it to
be here.

HECTOR   But I don't see why you find this so awful, my dear, you
are peculiar.

*the river flows steadily downward along a steep
incline*

Men and women separate.

*perhaps of some two hundred feet, but what helps
to make them so violent,*

**Each one receives, for papers and money, for car, ho-
tel, and house keys a little metal box whose tiny key
you have to hang around your neck on a hemp necklace.**

*is that from Lake Erie for a distance of almost six
leagues,*

They take you to an individual stall, where they ask you to undress completely.

> *is that, all the way to the cataract, the river flows steadily downward,*

If you insist, you can keep on your underpants.

> *in such a way that at the very edge of the cascade . . .*

Then you put on a pair of clumsy pajamas, faded and mended.

> *from Lake Erie along a steep incline,*

You put on and lace up slippers of thick cloth.

> *it is less a river, all the way to the cataract, for a distance of almost six leagues*

And last you put on the big yellow-gold waterproof hood.

> *than an impetuous sea, the river, with the result that at the very edge of the cascade . . .*

Slightly nervous,

> *whose hundred thousand torrents*

you entrust the little box to the desk,

> *flow steadily downward along a steep incline,*

you come out into the sun,

—automobiles starting up—
—thunder—
—dance music—

loud, as four o'clock strikes, fairly loud

> *—creaking—*
> *—wind howling—*
> *—rain—*

> *it is less a river than an impetuous sea,*

and you sit down on a bench among the group beginning to form to await the next guide.

rush

The cold of the waterproof on your skin

for a distance of almost six leagues,

makes you feel

whose hundred thousand torrents rush

naked,

toward the gaping mouth of a chasm,

without pockets,

with the result that at the very edge of the cascade

without identification,

toward the gaping mouth of a chasm, the cataract,

ELMER   We are the only Negroes.

in pajamas among these normal men who walk along in their jackets and shoes.

FLOSSIE   I see some Negro newlyweds coming back; it's all right.

the cataract,

is everything okay?   ANDREW

GERTRUDE   I am crazy.

it is less a river than an impetuous sea,

People look at each other with an anxious smile.

divides,

everything's okay.   BETTINA

HECTOR   You kept all your rings on!

divides into two branches

Well!   CLEM

GERTRUDE   That, yes! I may be crazy, but not to that point! They're not the least afraid of getting drenched.

whose hundred thousand torrents rush,

it's making us young again.   DOROTHY

HECTOR   This is really the first time you've been down there?

into two branches and curves,

GERTRUDE   Yes, little love, but do you know that it isn't very nice of you to ask that, after all I've told you? I'm crazy, I'm completely crazy: all my makeup and my whole hairdo! You're going to find me aged ten years; you will notice . . .

and curves,

The guide comes for the pilgrims, bantering with them.

toward the gaping mouth of a chasm,

HECTOR   People say this makes you young again.

into a horseshoe of about half a mile around.

The guide closes the elevator doors, and it goes down into a well in the rock.

Between the two falls juts out an enormous rock, hollow underneath, which hangs with all its pines over the chaos of the waves of about half a mile around, and curves,

All the yellow waterproofs rub one against the other.

the mass of the river which hurls itself southward bulges,

You grope for the key on your chest.

between the two falls juts out an enormous rock into a horseshoe of about half a mile around,

The doors open onto a long gently inclined corridor

and becomes rounded like a vast cylinder at the point of leaving the shore hollow underneath, between the two falls juts out an enormous rock,

which leads in the distance to the glaring damp daylight,

— machine-gun sprays of water —
— booming —
— footsteps on damp wood —

very loud, as five o'clock strikes, loud

—waterproof clothing rubbing—
—automobiles starting up—
—thunder—

> *then unrolls in a sheet of snow which hangs hollow*
> *underneath and glistens in the sun with all the*
> *colors of the prism*

**then, walking along the cliff above the debris, under
the foundation layers of broken stones,**

> *with all its pines, which hangs with all its pines*
> *over the chaos of the waves,*

**you come to a complex system of stairs and terraces
of mossy wood, which form a detour around an enormous rock fallen from the wall centuries ago.**

> *the one falling toward the north over the chaos of*
> *the waves,*

**One behind the other you climb into more and more
damp regions, the shower bath is more and more
violent.**

> *the mass of the river descends in a fearful darkness,*
> *the mass of the river hurls itself like a pillar of*
> *water from the flood,*

**Amusing signs have been arranged among the pebbles
and dripping vegetation:**

> *which hurls itself, bulges southward and becomes*
> *rounded like a vast cylinder,*

"Watch Out for Pickpockets!"

> *countless rainbows curve southward at the point of*
> *leaving the shore,*

**You become aware again then of the fact that you have
no pockets,**

> *and cross above the abyss,*

that you are in pajamas,

> *bulge,*

that all these people are in pajamas under their yellow waterproofs.

then unroll in a sheet

You see them laugh, but you can no longer hear them.

whose dreadful booming can be heard for sixty miles around, the waves become rounded like a vast cylinder of snow and glisten in the sun, striking the shaken rock at the point of leaving the shore, then unroll in a sheet of all the colors of the prism, splash back up in whirlwinds of snow-foam and glisten;

You sense that they are feeling for the key on their chest.

the one falling toward the north resembles thick smoke and glistens, descends in a fearful darkness like a pillar of a vast forest fire of pines in the sun of water;

You continue to climb.

wild walnut trees of all the colors of the flood, rocks cut into the form of a prism, rainbows of phantoms adorn the scene;

It becomes more and more slippery.

the one falling toward the north . . .

A fleece of trampled moss ripples over the ramps and steps.

Countless, the eagles

You have to struggle to move forward.

descend in a fearful darkness, curve, swept along . . .

An extraordinary odor of ozone arises, goes to your head.

like a pillar . . .

The bravest hold their faces up to the machine-gun spray of water.

And cross by the air current over the abyss of air

**The falls which ricochet this way full in your face are
called "The Bridal Veil."**

*from the flood whose dreadful booming descends in
spirals.*

**Climbing back up from the cave of the winds, each
retrieves his papers and money from his little box,**

*Countless rainbows are formed in the depths
of the chasm and*

**puts back on his shirt and socks, ties his tie, or gets
into her girdle and pulls up her stockings,**

curve and cross.

wipes his face again.

To hear the badgers over the abyss . . .

A little lipstick perhaps.

For sixty . . .

**Completely silent, the couples find each other again
dressed quite ordinarily; they look over at the still dry
yellow pilgrims who wait seated in front of the door,**

Hang by their flexible tails . . .

some new drenched pilgrims who are returning,

Whose thousand . . .

**and go away casting a glance at the souvenir counters
spread out in the other part of the building,**

Third Parenthesis of JULY

    (Story of the Shirt)

Do you want a flag?	ANDREW
Do you remember that set of dishes we bought?	CLEM
Dreadful . . .	READER
American or Canadian?	BETTINA
It didn't last long.	DOROTHY
Around . . .	
A flag with a waterfall.	ANDREW
We got some bowls and some plates.	CLEM
From a branch . . .	
To put on our car?	BETTINA
And some little salad plates, too.	DOROTHY
Booming . . .	
Or in our room.	ANDREW
The quality probably has been improved since then.	CLEM
The low waves . . .	

ANNOUNCER **Flags, hairbrushes, plates,**

Can be heard . . .

What size? BETTINA

I think we have only one chipped DOROTHY
one left. It must be in the refrigerator, and the picture is almost
worn off.

Striking the shaken rock splashes back up in whirl-
winds of foam . . .

If it's for the car, it shouldn't be too ANDREW
big.

ELMER Do you remember that shirt the daughter of one of my
bosses brought me back from the falls?

To catch . . .

Maybe it would be better to buy BETTINA
something more useful.

FLOSSIE She didn't bring it herself, she simply put it in the mail
with a note. She didn't have time. We never saw her
again. We never saw her husband again.

For sixty miles around, the waves striking the
rock . . .

Plates? ANDREW

I don't see any more engraved CLEM
glasses. I remember we wanted to
buy some, but they were much too
expensive for us at the time; it
wasn't in this shop anyway.

which rising above the trees resemble the thick
smoke of a vast forest fire of pines, of wild walnuts,
of cut rocks . . .

We don't have enough money to BETTINA
buy a whole set of these plates; it
wouldn't be sensible.

But they still have the same kind of DOROTHY

shirts. You insisted on taking one
back for your father's gardener.

In the abyss . . .

ANDREW

I'm not talking about a whole set; I
only mean one plate that we could
put on the mantle for a souvenir.

ELMER Before we even opened the package it had begun
to fade.

*Shaken splashes back up in whirlwinds of foam
which rising . . .*

BETTINA

But then it wouldn't really be something useful and it would be so
much more of a souvenir if it were
something we could use every day.

FLOSSIE I washed it and washed it and washed it until there was
nothing at all left of the picture or the writing, and then
I dyed it dark purple.

Into phantom forms adorn the scene of eagles.

ANDREW

Not necessarily every day, but holi-
days. We could buy two and every
Sunday you could serve our break-
fast on those plates.

CLEM

Did he ever go to the falls himself?

The carcasses . . .

BETTINA

Then we would need some little
plates and we could see if they don't
have some teacups, too.

DOROTHY

I don't remember.

*Above the trees like the thick smoke of a vast forest
fire of pines . . .*

ELMER One day, the boss's wife said to me, "Did you like that
shirt my daughter brought back to you from the falls?"
"Oh, yes, ma'am," I said. "I wear it almost every day."
I had the shirt on at the time.

CLEM And when you gave it to the gardener, he put it on once to please you, but at heart he didn't like it very much.

Walnut trees swept along by the current, broken . . .

FLOSSIE But you couldn't wear it very long.

DOROTHY Are you sure he actually wore it once? Besides, since then, we haven't really seen them again. It's too bad. Because we simply must take something back to our gardener, and I wonder if he, too, wouldn't like a shirt, you see, like this one.

Wild rocks cut into the form of phantoms of air descend in spirals to the depths of the chasm . . .

ELMER I tore it up that very evening.

Elks adorn the scene of eagles, and badgers hang by flexible tails at the end of a low branch . . .

CLEM Maybe we didn't pick out one in a loud enough color.

And bears swept along by the current of air descend in spirals to the depths of the chasm and badgers hang by their tails

FLOSSIE It made me some dishrags.

flexible at the end of a low branch

DOROTHY What we need especially, I think, is something good and substantial which isn't likely to tear the first time he tries it on.

to catch in the abyss the broken carcasses of the elks and of the bears.

V

The Floodlight Displays

Track A: Skip the parentheses.

Tracks BC: Read "Maid of the Mist," but omit the lines of Alex, Betsy, Clifford, Deirdre, Emil and Florence.

Track D: Read "Maid of the Mist," omitting the lines of Alex, Betsy, Clifford and Deirdre.

Track E: Read "Maid of the Mist" and "Postcards," omitting, in these two parentheses, the lines of Alex, Betsy, Clifford, Deirdre, Emil and Florence.

Track F: Read "Maid of the Mist" and "Postcards," omitting, in these two parentheses, the lines of Alex, Betsy, Clifford and Deirdre.

Track G: Read "Maid of the Mist," omitting the lines of Alex and Betsy.

Track H: Read "Story of the Ashtray," "Maid of the Mist" and "Postcards," omitting, in the two last parentheses, the lines of Alex and Betsy.

Track I: Read "Maid of the Mist."

Track J: Read everything.

in the center:

loud:

ANNOUNCER

at left:

fairly loud:

GENE: old madam

HUMPHREY: gigolo

at right:

IRRLING: vile seducer

JENNY: easy prey

in the center:

not too loud:

READER

at left:

fairly soft:

EMIL and FLORENCE: Negro gardeners

at right:

soft:

CLIFFORD and DEIRDRE: old married couple

very soft:

ALEX and BETSY: "just-marrieds"

Emil, Florence, Clifford, Deirdre, Alex and Betsy appear only in the parentheses.

If the left-hand channel is closed, Gene and Humphrey can still be heard, softly; Emil and Florence will disappear. If the right-hand channel is closed, Irrling and Jenny can still be heard, softly; Clifford and Deirdre, Alex and Betsy will disappear.

Little Prelude for six o'clock

In time with the first notes of the Westminster carillon;
fairly loud, can be heard:

        in the center:

at left:

            at right:

        not too loud:

fairly soft:

            soft:

      —door slamming—

            —booming—

      —shower—

—horn honking—

          —deep sigh—

              —footsteps on damp wood—

      —sob—

      —curtain flapping—

              —machine-gun spray of water—

      —windowpane vibrating—

—trickling—

—groan—

—jingling—

—ice clinking in a glass—

When Alex and Betsy speak, one of the left-hand
sounds resumes its original volume; when Clifford and
Deirdre speak, one of the left-hand sounds assumes a
volume setting one lower than before; when Emil and
Florence speak, one of the right-hand sounds drops
two settings below the original. Since one may consider
that a fairly loud sound effect actually covers any words
spoken fairly soft, for the motionless listener, but
only for him; in a normal setting, the voices of Emil and
Florence are covered during "Maid of the Mist," but
one need only move around a little, or lower the right-
hand channel a little, to reveal them.

— trickling —
— horns honking —
— jingling —

fairly loud, with the last notes of the carillon as six
o'clock strikes, not too loud, among the following lines:

> *— machine-gun sprays of water —*
> *— footsteps on damp wood —*
> *— booming —*

First Parenthesis of AUGUST

(Story of the Ashtray)

They,

ANNOUNCER **decanters, shirts, ties, ashtrays,**

the mass of the river of the bears,

EMIL And this ashtray like the one your neighbor brought back last year! She's so proud of it!

are formed by the Niagara River which hurls itself and which springs southward,

FLORENCE Do you want an ashtray?

bulges with the elks of Lake Erie,

EMIL No. Maybe we could take it to the preacher. We could have a little party when we get back. We could invite your neighbor.

and becomes rounded like a vast broken cylinder,

The hour passes.

and empties,

FLORENCE He will certainly be very touched. Then we should obviously get the next smaller size.

at the point of leaving the shore, to catch the car-

casses in the Ontario, then unrolls, low, at about nine miles in a sheet, at the end of a branch of the latter lake of flexible snow.

The day passes.

The falls are . . .

The month passes.

And glistens.

ANNOUNCER   **It is late afternoon.**

    And the badgers hang by their tails.   READER

It is still very warm.

    Their height in the sun of the vertical chasm with
    all the colors perhaps in the depths of the prism.

The rays are already golden.

    In spirals of about two hundred feet the one falling
    toward the north descends, eagles swept along by
    the air current descend.

Newlyweds of the day before covered with sweat,

    But what helps to make them so violent is that, in a
    fearful darkness, rocks cut into phantom forms
    adorn the scene from Lake Erie all the way to the
    cataract . . .

**newlyweds of this morning, in shorts, bermudas or
pedal-pushers,**

    Like a pillar of wild water, the river of the flood;
    like the smoke of a vast forest fire, of pines, of wal-
    nut trees . . .

**old married couples who had come when they got
married and those who had not been able to come,**

Flow steadily countless rainbows which rise above the trees,

with their white or black straw hats,

downward bend in whirlwinds of foam

with their white or black faces covered with sweat,

along a steep incline, and cross above the abyss; the water splashes back up

rather mature married women, skinny or fleshy,

for a distance of almost six leagues, whose dreadful booming can be heard for sixty miles around, striking the shaken rock,

with too much makeup, with dyed or discolored hair,

with the result that at the very edge of the cascade, striking the shaken rock, the water splashes back up for sixty miles around,

with shadows under their eyes, eyebrows thickened with pencil,

it is less a river than a sea in whirlwinds of foam whose dreadful booming can be heard,

jingling,

impetuous whose hundred thousand torrents rising above the trees curve and cross over the abyss,

with necklaces, bracelets, pendants,

rush like countless rainbows,

— sobs —
— deep sighs —
— showers —

loud, as seven o'clock strikes, fairly loud

— doors slamming —
— trickling —
— horns honking —

dark glasses, alligator cigarette cases, which they twiddle nervously,

toward the gaping mouth of a chasm, the smoke from the flood . . .

and very long cigarette holders which they tap with their little fingers,

the cataract of a vast forest fire of water

their rayon blouses stained with sweat,

is divided into pillars;

accompanied by very sunburned young men who are not their sons,

two pines, a branch, and walnut trees,

in loose-fitting shirts printed with fiery horses or revolvers,

as wild rocks cut into phantom forms curve,

go over a crosswalk—the sun is setting—and reach Moon Island between the great American Falls and The Bridal Veil.

in a fearful darkness,

Leaning on the railing,

into a horseshoe,

a man no longer middle-aged,

adorn the scene,

a carnation in his buttonhole,

descend

a jacket of imitation alpaca

for about half a mile,

a plaid corduroy hat,

eagles swept along toward the north by the current falling,

covered with sweat,

in a circle of air, descend in spirals.

gloats over a young girl

—ice clinking in glasses—
—groans—
—windowpanes vibrating—

very loud, as eight o'clock strikes, loud

> *—curtains flapping—*
> *—sobs—*
> *—deep sighs—*

The one,

who could easily be his daughter,

between the two,

in blue jeans,

in the depths of the chasm of the prism . . .

sweater,

Falls in the depths of the chasm

a big cloth hat decorated with raffia flowers,

with all the colors . . .

covered with sweat.

Juts out in spirals

> And suppose we go down to the   IRRLING
> cave of the winds?
>
> It's a little late, I think.   JENNY

in the twilight

Second Parenthesis of AUGUST

(Maid of the Mist)

Oh, you have the program! May IRRLING
I . . .

Why, of course. JENNY

an enormous hollow rock. READER

Well, then, perhaps we could go IRRLING
down as far as the boat?

Well, it stops at twilight. JENNY

Eagles swept along by the air current descend and
glisten;

You saw the name of the boat? IRRLING

The "Virgin of the Mist." JENNY

underneath

You can't read; it isn't the "Virgin," IRRLING
it's the "Maid of the Mist."

Do you know why? JENNY

adorn the scene of soot

They thought of you. IRRLING

Who did? JENNY

which hangs with all its pines cut into phantom forms,

The Indians. They say it's an old Indian legend. IRRLING

Can you tell it to me? JENNY

then unrolls in a sheet

But the Indians were thinking of you. IRRLING

How? JENNY

over the chaos of the pines, the wild walnut trees,

It's as if . . . IRRLING

Like a dream? JENNY

at the point of leaving the shore of waves;

ANNOUNCER **One comes back from Moon Island to Goat Island under The Bridal Veil.**

like the smoke of a vast forest fire, a vast cylinder,

It's as if they had seen you in a dream. IRRLING

An apparition? JENNY

the mass of the whirlwind of foam rising above the trees,

Then one crosses back over a bridge to Green Island, formerly Isle of the Bath.

like a river which hurls itself,

With your eyes and your hair. IRRLING

Tell me. JENNY

splashes back up in a bulge and becomes rounded,

Then another bridge, and one walks along the river and the left-hand gorge.

southward can be heard for sixty miles around, striking the shaken rock, the water

I don't know all the details.   IRRLING

I don't need all the details.   JENNY

bulges

To the right, lawns with flowerbeds of canna lilies

Gold   ALEX

around

dotted with carmine.   BETSY

in the twilight,

But you will be here to inspire me.   IRRLING

which hurls itself southward

Amaranth   CLIFFORD

and becomes rounded.

striped with yellow.   DEIRDRE

in the deep twilight,

The mass of the river like a vast cylinder.

It's so nice of you to have given me   JENNY
this trip!

Sixty . . .

EMIL   Red-lead-colored,

in the last twilight,

Over the chaos of the waves,

LORENCE   cardinal-colored.

at the point of leaving the shore,

in the remains of twilight.

whose dreadful booming can be heard by all the pines,

EMIL   Beautiful young rolled-up leaves

GENE   And all that—you like all that, you do—you don't
need to be made young!

> *then unroll in a sheet of snow and glisten in the moonlight,*

FLORENCE   as around the finger of their gardener.

> *curve and cross above the abyss*

HUMPHREY   But you — it really has made you young again!

> *with . . .*

>   Without you, I would find this a   IRRLING
> frightful place, you know. I have
> never been happy here.

Evening.

GENE   Because I seemed to you very old before, very wrinkled, very faded, very decayed, admit it!

> *Of all the colors of the darkness,*

>   Because you came here when . . .   JENNY

> *countless storm clouds*

HUMPHREY   Be quiet.

> *which hang . . .*

>   Yes. Oh, why talk about all that,   IRRLING
> bore you with my regrets, my
> wasted life . . .

All the breaths of evening.

GENE   But I don't know why I tease you like that since all these young people who have just been married . . .

> *The one falling toward the north descends in a fearful darkness*

>   Your wasted life?   JENNY

> *like a pillar of water from the flood,*

HUMPHREY   Be quiet.

> *underneath,*

>   Not entirely wasted since you have   IRRLING
> come, since everything takes on
> new colors because of you.

All the lights of the two cities.

GENE They don't need to be made young again, but I don't want you to look at them . . .

> *like a pillar of water from the flood,*

Let's go . . .   JENNY

> *the one falling toward the north descends in a fearful darkness.*

UMPHREY Be quiet.

> *An enormous hollow rock,*

Since everything takes on the as-   IRRLING
pect I longed for before, the first
time . . .

All the electric signs.

GENE And if you looked at them carefully, you would soon see that they, too, need to be made young again . . .

> *countless rainbows*

Oh, yes . . .   JENNY

> *of all the colors of the darkness*

UMPHREY Be quiet.

> *jut out,*

It's that I expected so much, you   IRRLING
know, I was in the ardor of all my
twenty years, and she was not as
beautiful as you . . .

All the automobile headlights.

GENE And all these young women who are already married, you ought not to look at them . . .

> *curve and cross above the abyss*

Let's go . . .   JENNY

> *in the moonlight*

UMPHREY Be quiet.

between the two falls whose dreadful booming can
be heard for sixty miles around,

> Because you are beautiful, I don't　IRRLING
> know if you know it, if people have
> told you . . .

All the insects of an August evening buzz.

GENE　They are not for you anymore, and then I can assure
you that their skin is already faded . . .

and glisten

> Let's go . . .　JENNY

in a horseshoe of about half a mile around.

HUMPHREY　Be quiet.

Striking the rock

> But she was beautiful, too, a differ-　IRRLING
> ent sort of beauty, less touching,
> and she knew it, and, oh, I can't tell
> you . . .

A whole storm cloud of insects around the streetlights.

GENE　You are all that I like here; the fact that you are here is
all I like here.

in a sheet of soot,

> Let's go . . .　JENNY

which curves

HUMPHREY　We could stay a little longer; you would see; you would
relax.

shaken,

> She still has some traces of her　IRRLING
> beauty, but from the very first day
> here, what disillusionment, how she
> made me suffer!

> Let's go . . .　JENNY

—jingling—
—machine-gun sprays of water—
—footsteps on damp wood—

loud, as nine o'clock strikes, very loud
—booming—
—ice clinking in glasses—
—groans—

NOUNCER **In the month of August,**

    unrolls   READER

       I don't know if I should tell IRRLING
       you . . .

    in two branches,

       Why, of course!   JENNY

    the water splashes back up,

at nine o'clock,

       I should leave you all your beautiful IRRLING
       dreams . . .

    divides in whirlwinds of foam rising above the
    trees,

       Let's go . . .   JENNY

all the lights are put out,

> And not unfold the resentment, the   IRRLING
> despair of a man who has sought
> happiness in all sorts of affairs with-
> out finding it and who abandons
> hope of finding it . . .

at the point of leaving the shore;

> But you must not abandon hope!   JENNY

the cataract,

the floodlight displays begin,

> *like the smoke of a vast forest fire,*

while in the street of the falls,

> *like a vast cylinder*

among the restaurants and movies, couples more or less suited

> *toward the gaping mouth of a chasm.*

in the souvenir shops scrutinize, finger, compare,

> *Pines, wild walnut trees, rocks cut into phantom forms . . .*

—showers—
—doors slamming—
—trickling—

fairly loud, as ten o'clock strikes, loud

> *—horns honking—*
> *—jingling—*
> *—machine-gun sprays of water—*

GENE   How ugly all this is! Could there be something that might tempt you among all these horrors?

> *Becomes rounded . . .*

HUMPHREY   What's that?

little naked porcelain women whose breasts come off to make salt and pepper shakers,

GENE   Medallions.

Rush . . .

HUMPHREY   What are they for?

bedlamps, medallions of butterfly wings, buttons,

Adorn the scene of eagles . . .

GENE   Nothing. They are souvenirs. You hang it up in your bedroom. Of course, I want you to have souvenirs, but that, that isn't for you.

Torrents . . .

HUMPHREY   What is it made of?

table napkins, tapestries, postcards.

GENE   Butterfly wings.

Swept along . . .

HUMPHREY   Really butterfly wings?

GENE   Yes, exotic butterflies that they catch in Brazil or Guatemala, somewhere.

Bulge . . .

HUMPHREY   And you don't think it's pretty?

GENE   You're surely not going to try to make me believe . . .

A thousand . . .

HUMPHREY   No, but it's funny.

The floodlight displays:

Third Parenthesis of AUGUST

(Postcards)

GENE   If that really amuses you, if that's really your whim . . .

EMIL   Cardinal-colored,

HUMPHREY   Oh! Why no, that or something else, you know . . .

FLOSSIE   red-lead-colored.

Southward . . .   READER

Striped with yellow.   CLIFFORD

GENE   You are marvelous; I would like to kiss you right here in front of everyone.

Amaranth.   DEIRDRE

HUMPHREY   Don't talk so loud.

Dotted with carmine.   ALEX

Southward . . .

Gold.   BETSY

GENE   You are so inexperienced, a real little savage. Everything seems wonderful to you. And that, look at that; those are table napkins, table napkins with waterfalls printed on them! No, but imagine how someone would look wiping his mouth with such a thing!

Coral pink changing to pink.   DEIRDRE

HUMPHREY   Why?

Deep red clouded with black.   CLIFFORD

Impetuous whose hundred . . .

FLOSSIE   Scarlet red and yellow gold

GENE   It's true that if it were you, I would try to make my-self like things like that, but I would just as soon . . . there, really, I would just as soon give you something else.

EMIL   like the "Talisman" rose.

HUMPHREY   You know, I don't exactly know what I would do with table napkins.

Silvery pink.   BETSY

Descend in spirals . . .

White splotched with purple.   ALEX

GENE   Postcards.

FLOSSIE   Dark purplish red tinged with brilliant garnet and shaded with maroon

HUMPHREY   Yes?

EMIL   like a Chinese peony.

Which hurls itself . . .

Sky-blue mauve.   DEIRDRE

GENE   Your parents aren't expecting you to write them, are they?

Rosy mauve.   CLIFFORD

HUMPHREY   Oh, no!

FLOSSIE   Violet with black spots

It is less a river than a sea . . .

EMIL   like the "Purple Splendor" rhododendron.

GENE   You haven't told me what you told them. Tell me what you would have told them.

BETSY   Dark heliotrope and rosy lilac.

HUMPHREY   Lies . . .

ALEX   Lemon yellow and amaranth red.

In the depths of the river . . .

FLOSSIE   Blue

GENE   You're a tricky little savage. And to think I have such a spineless son! He isn't one to be able to tell me lies.

EMIL   like the pallida iris.

HUMPHREY   You think not?

DEIRDRE   Lavender pink.

With the result that at the very edge of the chasm and of the cascade . . .

CLIFFORD   Purplish red.

GENE   He doesn't have any lies; he couldn't have any lies.

FLOSSIE   Bluish lilac

HUMPHREY   You think that.

Masses flow steadily downward along a steep incline for a distance of almost six leagues . . .

GENE   He was spoiled by his father and his school.

EMIL   like your lilac.

HUMPHREY   Which one?

Badgers there . . .

GENE   He doesn't like anything, he isn't interested in anything.

The cataract, the river . . .

HUMPHREY   That you know of.

Hang all the way to . . .

GENE   He has dim eyes; he doesn't have beautiful eyes all inexperienced and a little tricky, like yours, which make one pardon everything.

By Lake Erie . . .

HUMPHREY Well?

Their tails from . . .

GENE Well, I'm going to give you some postcards just the same, because these are fairly nicely done, don't you think? Usually the colors are so ugly, but just for once . . .

From the end of a branch . . .

HUMPHREY I think the colors are even better in the slides.

But what helps to make them so violent, is that . . .

ANNOUNCER **pillows, slides, miniature toilets,**

Low, their vertical height may be of about two hundred feet . . .

GENE Yes, but you have to have a projector for them. I am going to buy you some postcards.

To catch the waterfall in the abyss . . .

HUMPHREY You insist on it?

Are found the carcasses of this latter lake, broken . . .

GENE I will buy you whatever you want, too, but these postcards, when you are home again, you will send them to me, won't you, you promise me, you will send them to me?

And empty into the Ontario at about nine miles . . .

HUMPHREY Of course.

From the elks and from the bears . . .

GENE Oh, don't worry, you don't need to write on them. The better to remember, that will be enough.

HUMPHREY The better to remember.

VI

The Rooms

Tracks A B: Skip the parentheses.

Tracks C D G I: Read "The Bachelor's Invocation."

Track E: Read everything, but omit, in "Irving's Over-
           tures," the lines of Alec, Bessie, Cary, Dora,
           Edmund and Frieda.

Track F: Read everything, but omit, in "Irving's Over-
           tures," the lines of Alec, Bessie, Cary and
           Dora.

Track H: Read everything, but omit, in "Irving's Over-
           tures," the lines of Alec and Bessie.

Track J: Read everything.

CAST OF CHARACTERS

in the center:

loud:

ANNOUNCER

     at right:

     fairly loud:

     IRVING: vile seducer

     JANE: easy prey

at left:

not too loud:

GERDA: old madam

HUBERT: gigolo

     READER

fairly soft:

EDMUND and FRIEDA: Negro gardeners

     KEITH: young man alone

     soft:

     CARY and DORA: old married couple

     very soft:

     ALEC and BESSIE: "just-marrieds"

Gerda, Hubert, Irving, Jane and Keith appear only in the parentheses.

If the right-hand channel is closed, Irving and Jane can still be heard softly; Keith, Cary, Dora, Alec, Bessie are silenced.

If the left-hand channel is closed, Gerda and Hubert can still be heard very softly; Edmund and Frieda are silenced.

Little Prelude for eleven o'clock in the evening

In time with the first seven notes of the Westminster carillon, loud, can be heard:

    in the center:

at left:

                at right:

    fairly loud:

not too loud:

                fairly soft:

    — kiss —

                — horn honking —

    — branch whispering —

— sigh —

    — animal movement —

                — trickling —

    — breathing —

                — machine-gun spray of water —

— laughter —

                — shower —

    — heart beating —

—ice clinking in a glass—

—panting—

—thunder—

—grunting—

When Alec and Bessie speak, one of the sound effects indicated in the text on the left-hand resumes its original volume; when Cary and Dora speak, one of the left-hand sounds assumes a volume setting one lower than formerly; when Keith speaks, one of the left-hand sounds drops two settings lower. When Edmund and Frieda speak, one of the right-hand sounds drops two settings lower.

—sighs—
—ice clinking in glasses—
—showers—

loud, with the last notes of the carillon, as eleven o'clock
strikes, fairly loud, among the following lines:

— machine-gun sprays of water —
— trickling —
— horns honking —

First Parenthesis of SEPTEMBER

(Irving's Overtures)

But just look at that, the ideas IRVING
people get, a toilet, yes, it really is
a tiny toilet!

Well, yes. JANE

But they are formed by the river of the flood, READER

NNOUNCER **The hour passes.**

GERDA Just the same you must pay attention.

Are you blushing? I shouldn't show IRVING
you things like that.

HUBERT The better to remember.

Why, yes, why ever not? JANE

what helps to make them so violent, Niagara which
springs from Lake Erie, and empties like a pillar
of water,

GERDA You'll send them to me while I'm on vacation with my
husband, one a week, and my husband will see from
time to time a picture of the falls.

But I would like so much to give IRVING
you something as a souvenir.

HUBERT One a week.

                              Oh, no. Why?   JANE

            is that into the Ontario, in a fearful darkness,

The night passes.

            from Lake Erie descends for about nine miles,

GERDA And that will remind him, perhaps, that will worry his
       mind, he will wonder, but no, that will accomplish
       nothing.

            *all the way to the cataract of the latter lake, the
            one falling toward the north,*

                        Some trifle, a plaything, something   IRVING
                        which perhaps will make you think
                        of me some evening when you are
                        tired.

            is the river with all the colors of the darkness . . .

HUBERT Whatever you wish.

The month passes.

                        Oh, so many evenings . . .   JANE

            flow the falls in the moonlight;

GERDA I don't know why I'm telling you all this. You will
       send them to me very faithfully, won't you, promise?

            steadily their vertical height glistens;

                        We'll go have something to drink   IRVING
                        together; we'll say good night to
                        each other in the hotel corridor.

            *downward along a steep incline, perhaps of about
            two hundred feet, for a distance of almost six
            leagues, but in a sheet of snow;*

HUBERT Of course; I promise. They have cameras, too.

September.

                        Oh, I want to go see the floodlight   JANE
                        displays again.

with the result that at the very edge of the cascade,
what helps to make them so violent at the point of
leaving the shore then unrolls,

GERDA Well, really, it would be better to buy them somewhere other than here.

it is less a river than an impetuous sea, is that,
from Lake Erie all the way to the cataract, the
river like a vast cylinder

Of course, we'll go see the dis- IRVING
plays again, but after that we'll
have to separate.

whose hundred thousand torrents rush, flow stead-
ily, bulge and become rounded toward the gaping
mouth of a chasm; steadily downward along a
steep incline, the mass of the river which hurls it-
self southward;

HUBERT Then, don't you think we could go in?

Still very hot.

That's how it will have to be. JANE

the cataract divides into two branches and curves
for a distance of almost six leagues with all its
pines over the chaos of the waves,

FRIEDA And the bees buzzing in their tea bush in the midst of
walls of skin.

in a horseshoe of about half a mile around, with the
result that at the very edge of the cascade juts out
an enormous rock hollow underneath which hangs

I will have to see the door of your IRVING
room closing on one last smile
from you, won't I?

between the two falls, it is less a river than a sea
of about half a mile around between the two falls,

EDMUND My buds of milky coral.

Heavy.

That's how it will have to be.   JANE

juts out, impetuous, whose hundred thousand tor-
rents rush and curve in a horseshoe,

FRIEDA   Their green blood on your rough fingers.

an enormous rock hollow toward the gaping mouth
of a chasm, the cataract divides into two branches

And I'll have to go back to mine to   IRVING
meet my solitude and my problems
again there.

underneath, the cataract divides toward the gap-
ing mouth of a chasm,

EDMUND   Farewell, my bronze leaves whom I have so watched
over!

Stormy.

That's how it will have to be.   JANE

which hangs in two branches whose hundred
thousand torrents rush,

Lilac.   DORA

with all its pines and bends, impetuous,

And then tomorrow, you know,   IRVING
we'll take the train again, both of us,
and it will be back to the office.

over the chaos of the waves in a horseshoe, it is
less a river than a sea,

Iris with tulip petals.   CARY

Storm clouds

Glazed,   ALEC

I know.   JANE

brilliant.   BESSIE

with reflections from the floodlights.

the mass of the river, of about half a mile around,

with the result that at the very edge of the cascade,

> We will see each other, you'll make   IRVING
> a little sign to me from time to time,
> and it's so you at least will make a
> little sign to me from time to time
> that I definitely want to give you
> something now.

which hurls itself between the two falls, with the result that at the very edge,

More and more clouds

> Peonies with iris petals.   DORA
>
> Oh, no . . .   JANE
>
> Roses with peony petals.   CARY

race by.

southward juts out an enormous rock hollow underneath the cascade,

ANNOUNCER **Lower and lower clouds**

                    Red,   ALEC

                    roses,   BESSIE

hide the moon.

                    bulges and becomes rounded like a vast cylinder   READER
                    which hangs, with the result that at the very edge
                    of the cascade,

Faster and faster storm clouds,

                    beautiful,   ALEC

above the last beams from the projectors, the last
shadings in the water.

                    very beautiful,   BESSIE

                    at the point of leaving the shore with all its pines,
                    it is less a river than a sea,

                    farewell, delicate,   ALEC

All the lights have been put out.

                    soft . . .   BESSIE

                    then unrolls in a sheet of soot over the chaos of
                    the impetuous waves;

Second Parenthesis of SEPTEMBER

(Irving's Grand Aria)

So that this trip which would have   IRVING
been such a relief for me, you
have no idea—oh, I had resigned
myself not to think of happiness
anymore, but now, in spite of myself, when I think of you . . . such
an oasis in my desert . . .

and glistens in the moonlight the mass of the river   READER
whose hundred thousand torrents rush

Let's go . . .   JANE

ANNOUNCER   **A lightning flash perhaps . . .**

with all the colors of darkness, which hurls itself
toward the gaping mouth of a chasm

Well, so you, too, might keep some-   IRVING
thing like a little emotion.

The spectacle ended, the whole crowd flows back
toward the hotels.

of darkness; the mass of the river bulges south-
ward

Oh, you may be sure . . .   JANE

The streetlights are lit again above the flower beds.

with all the colors,

A pillow, look at this pillow, feel IRVING
it, caress it, it's soft, isn't it, do you
like it?

A new flash of lightning over the shining river,

*and becomes rounded like a vast cylinder which
hurls itself southward and glistens in the moonlight,*

nibbled by clouds.

You know . . . JANE

at the point of leaving the shore, bulges

Lights of hotel bedrooms come on, on both sides.

You will put it on your bed, you IRVING
will slide it up close to you, and
the picture will refresh you.

*in a sheet of soot, then unrolls and becomes
rounded,*

The picture . . . JANE

*leaving the shore, then unrolls in a sheet of soot
like a vast cylinder,*

The lights of the other houses are all already out.

*at the point of . . . and glistens in the moonlight
at the point of leaving the shore*

You see, there are silver spangles, IRVING
they're not really silver spangles,
but it's almost silver, it's exactly
like silver.

*like a cylinder of all the colors of darkness, then
unrolls,*

I think it must cost a lot. JANE

The electric signs go out one by one.

bulges southward and becomes rounded, the one fall-
ing in a sheet of soot,

A lot! Don't you believe it! I'm   IRVING
not very rich, I think I should tell
you that right away . . .

the mass of the river which hurls itself toward the
north descends in a fearful darkness and glistens
in the moonlight,

Clouds.

And I . . .   JANE

waves like a pillar of water from the flood with
all the colors of darkness,

Anyway, you know about how much   IRVING
I can earn at the office, and I hardly
have any other resources.

over the chaos of the thousand arches, the one
falling,

Of course . . .   JANE

The crowd is leaving the movies,

which hangs with all its pines in the sky toward
the north,

My family was once very well off   IRVING
but was the victim of one of the
crashes.

underneath curves, descends

looks anxiously at the dark sky.

Mine . . .   JANE

hollow, and crosses in a fearful darkness;

And that's why I find myself today   IRVING
in a position which is somewhat . . .
subordinate.

an enormous rock over the abyss, like a pillar,

But soon . . .   JANE

Scarcely a trace of one in the midst of the coursing clouds.

juts out, striking with water,

But, really, it's nothing. Happily   IRVING
for me, I can give you better
things than that. You like it?

between the two falls, the rock shaken from the flood;

Pillows, postcards, tapestries . . .

It's that . . .   JANE

in a horseshoe of about half a mile around, the water of the flood

I see that you want it, take it, at   IRVING
least that, be nice. And the tapestries, what would you think about
these tapestries?

divides into branches and curves, splashes back up a pillar of water;

Here is the rain.

But it's that . . .   JANE

the cataract in whirlwinds, fearful like the gaping mouth of a chasm of foam which descends,

You could use them as drapes, that   IRVING
would brighten your room.

whose hundred thousand torrents rush, rise above the trees of the north;

Here is the rain.   JANE

The movie lobbies are closing.

impetuous like the smoke of a vast forest fire, the one falling,

How many windows do you have?   IRVING
One day, if you're willing, I'll have
to come and see how you have fixed

them up, learn a little about how
you live . . .

it is less a river than a sea.

But of course, my dear sir, when-   JANE
ever you wish.

— branches whispering —
— kisses —
—thunder —

very loud, as midnight strikes, loud

— laughter —
— sighs —
— ice clinking in glasses —

ANNOUNCER   **The last souvenir shops close.**

Pines, wild walnut trees   READER

Rain beats on the windows of all the rooms.

of all the colors of darkness,

Only some dance halls and bars are still open.

with the result that at the very edge of the cascade,

Don't be afraid.   ALEC

rocks cut into phantom forms adorn the scene in the moonlight,

I'm not afraid.   BESSIE

The clouds are torn for a moment.

Are you afraid of the storm?   ALEC

Doors bang in the hotel corridors.

It isn't only the storm.   BESSIE

—panting—
—hearts beating—
—breathing—

loud, as one o'clock strikes, very loud

—animal movements—
—branches whispering—
—kisses—

for a distance of almost six leagues,

Are you through?   ALEC

All the showers in all the hotel bathrooms.

Wait a minute.   BESSIE

**All the air conditioners buzzing like swarms of enor-
mous flies, or enormous birds, with bloodshot eyes,
sharp-edged beaks, ripping talons.**

eagles,

Why are you clutching your dress-   ALEC
ing gown so tightly?

and glisten,

I can't seem to breathe anymore.   BESSIE

**On the windowpanes the hundred thousand torrents
streaming down.**

Shall I put out the light?   ALEC

steep,

I think that would be better.   BESSIE

swept along,

**Everything which streams over foreheads in cheap
hotels.**

in a sheet of sweat,

—machine-gun sprays of water—
—trickling—
—horns honking—

fairly loud, as two o'clock strikes, loud

—grunting—
—panting—
—hearts beating—

Are you asleep?   CARY

downward by an incline,

I can't.   DORA

In each night table a Gideon Bible.

by an air current,

It must be the storm.   CARY

then unroll,

It's a different storm.   DORA

Lightning, through all the streaming windowpanes, throws its light on the sheets,

the river flows steadily,

Disappointment?   CARY

descend

I think it's too late for us.   DORA

in the black night,

at the point of leaving the shore,

Shall I turn on the light?   CARY

the cataract

I think that would be better.   DORA

in the black rain;

in spirals

—laughter—

—sighs—
—ice clinking in glasses—

not too loud, as three o'clock strikes, fairly loud

> *— showers —*
> *— machine-gun sprays of water —*
> *— trickling —*

EDMUND   Do you want me to open the window?

> *like a vast cylinder*

FRIEDA   I think that will be better.

blood;

EDMUND   Storm.

> *all the way to the depths of the chasm,*

FRIEDA   Beautiful storm.

> *becomes rounded*

> My darling.   ALEC

rain of blood,

> Yes.   BESSIE

from Lake Erie,

> What I try to find again in the   CARY
> depths of your eyes,

> *and*

> fled away so far in the depths of   DORA
> your eyes.

rain of black blood,

> *and*

EDMUND   You've always loved a storm.

> *it is that*

FRIEDA   You've always been comfortable in a storm.

rain of old black blood in the night,

> *badgers*

Don't cry.   ALEC

bulge

It's nothing.   BESSIE

**blood of the massacred returning moaning in the
black night;**

so violent,

It's coming, it's getting close, I'm   CARY
finding you again.

hang

How far away you are!   DORA

— animal movements —
— branches whispering —
— kisses —

fairly soft, as four o'clock strikes, not too loud

— thunder —
— laughter —
— sighs —

**and through the open windows a puff of cool air slips
in.**

southward,

EDMUND   Beauty.

help to make them . . .

FRIEDA   Tongue of black gold.

by their flexible tails,

**The calm storm calms a little, recedes a little; the
clouds reveal little by little the moon, still lashing it,
still caressing it.**

Well!   ALEC

hurls itself,

Why are you laughing?   BESSIE

Less rain.

that which . . .

Keeps me from talking, makes me laugh, my darling.	ALEC
Oh, yes.	BESSIE

at the end . . .

Can do no more.	ALEC
Sleep.	BESSIE

which . . .

Don't cry anymore.	ALEC
I'm asleep.	BESSIE

but . . .

I love you.	ALEC
Be calm.	BESSIE

of a . . .

Very soft rain, now softer and softer, which fades away a song of rain of sweat of blood of sweet tears of night black pearls and of moon.

river . . .

Third Parenthesis of SEPTEMBER

(Irving's Triumph)

ANNOUNCER **In some rooms, ice still clinks in the bottom of glasses.**

but what helps to make them so violent . . . READER

GERDA Want something to drink?

branch . . .

HUBERT I suppose so.

All the dripping branches washed.

of . . .

Scotch? IRVING

No. JANE

is that . . .

Softly the leaves in the night moving at the end of their branches, losing their drops, receiving drops from other leaves and sending them on to still others, a cascade of dew.

low . . .

GERDA It will give you courage.

the mass . . .

HUBERT   But you, you're not drinking.

Dark.

from . . .

          I don't frighten you?   IRVING

to catch . . .

          No, but everything is turning JANE
around.

Obsession,

over the chaos of the waves . . .

GERDA   I'm already drunk.

Lake Erie . . .

HUBERT   Not enough.

which prowls

in the abyss . . .

          Stretch out on the bed, let me un- IRVING
dress you, let me.

*an enormous rock hollow underneath which hangs
with all its pines . . .*

          No, help me to go back to my room. JANE

in the booming night;

all the way to . . .

GERDA   I beg of you, please, why are you laughing?

the carcasses . . .

HUBERT   Come here.

groans in the night,

jut out . . .

          Why, you can't even stand up; IRVING
there, don't be afraid, don't cry,
I'm going to put out the light.

the cataract . . .

Don't leave me! JANE

tears in the night,

broken . . .

GERDA All that you want I'll give you, I promise you.

falls . . .

HUBERT Let me sleep, be quiet.

night,

divides . . .

Rest now, sleep. IRVING

Why are you laughing? JANE

the elks . . .

Fourth Parenthesis of SEPTEMBER

(The Bachelor's Invocation)

ANNOUNCER **deserted night, movement of animals in the parks; through the avenues washed clean a solitary figure walks,**

between the two, into two . . . READER

O all of you in your bedrooms en- KEITH
twined two by two,

and . . .

follows in his sleeplessness a very long road which curves,

into a horseshoe of about half a mile around . . .

o all of you chained naked flesh to KEITH
naked flesh, night unto night,

branches . . .

wavering in the fog while phantoms breathe,

bears . . .

behind all these black panes arous- KEITH
ing vice or love,

and curves . . .

and cocks an ear in the night across the booming,

    and curves . . .

        all your beating hearts, all your   KEITH
        mingled breaths, all your humors,
        salivas and tears,

    into two branches . . .

the booming night,

    into a horseshoe of about half a mile around . . .

        double choir of waters,   KEITH

    the cataract divides . . .

imperturbably impetuous, in the night,

    between the two falls . . .

        I listen for the oracle,   KEITH

    toward the gaping mouth of a chasm . . .

in the night where clouds are scattering,

    juts out . . .

        household gods of the continent,   KEITH
        prophetic sore in the slobbering
        overflow.

    whose hundred thousand torrents rush . . .

night unto night, entwining, embracing,

    an enormous rock hollow underneath . . .

        where I remain alone on watch,   KEITH
        drunk on water,

    it is less a river than an impetuous sea . . .

**washing the night of all its clouds, washing all the
filth from the shore,**

    which hangs with all its pines . . .

        and you, too, shivers of the trees,   KEITH
        deliver me,

with the result that at the very edge of the cas-
cade . . .

in the middle of the night,

    over the chaos of the waves,

        alone, but fleeing my solitude,   KEITH
        alone, but pursued by the demon of
        my solitude,

    the mass of the river,

panting by night,

    which hurls itself southward,

        tell me, who will deliver me from   KEITH
        my exile,

    bulges and becomes rounded

**stuttering by night, declaration by night, long entry
by night, long recording,**

    like a vast cylinder

        tell me, what lips will finally untie   KEITH
        these bonds of emptiness,

    at the point of leaving the shore,

at the embarkation in the night,

    then unrolls

        will finally unveil to me this secret   KEITH
        damp, this unhappiness more pre-
        cious than anything, this warmth,
        like other men . . .

    in a sheet of snow,

in the night.

    and glistens in the moonlight with all the colors
    of darkness

VII

The Awakenings

Tracks A B: Skip the parentheses.

Track C: Read "Daybreak," but omit the lines of Alan, Billie, Carrol, Dinah, Errol and Franny.

Track D: Read "Daybreak," omitting the lines of Alan, Billie, Carrol and Dinah.

Track E: Read everything, but omit, in the first two parentheses, the lines of Alan, Billie, Carrol, Dinah, Errol and Franny.

Track F: Read everything, but omit, in the first two parentheses, the lines of Alan, Billie, Carrol and Dinah.

Track G: Read "Daybreak," omitting the lines of Alan and Billie.

Track H: Read everything, but omit, in the first two parentheses, the lines of Alan and Billie.

Track I: Read "Daybreak."

Track J: Read everything.

in the center:

loud:

ANNOUNCER

fairly loud:

READER

at left:	at right:
not too loud:	not too loud:
IGOR: vile seducer	JUDY: easy prey
GEORGIA: old madam	HENRY: gigolo
fairly soft:	fairly soft:
ERROL: Negro gardener	FRANNY: Negro gardener's wife
LANA: young woman alone	
soft:	soft:
DINAH: white wife	CARROL: white husband
	KLAUS: young man alone
very soft:	very soft:
ALAN: "just-married"	BILLIE: "just-married"

All the couples are here "divorced": each character speaks as if he were alone.

If the right-hand channel is closed, Judy and Henry can still be heard, but very softly; Franny, Carrol, Klaus and Billie disappear.

If the left-hand channel is closed, Igor and Georgia can still be heard, but very softly; Errol, Lana, Dinah and Alan disappear.

It is to be noted that the change in balance transforms not only the relative volumes, nor only the number of characters present, but also their relations in space; if the right-hand channel is lowered, Franny, Carrol, Klaus and Billie remain at right before being silenced, but Judy and Henry move toward the left.

Little Prelude for five o'clock in the morning

In time with the first six notes of the Westminster carillon, very loud, can be heard:

in the center:

at left:

at right:

loud:

fairly loud:

not too loud:

—tree shivering—

—sigh—

—turnstile clicking—

—laughter—

—flag flapping—

—camera clicking—

—thunder—

—elevator machinery—

—foghorn—

—shower—

—whirlwind of a leaf—

—door banging—

  —animal movement—

—diesel engine—

  —breathing—

—birdcall—

When Alan and Dinah speak, one of the right-hand sounds resumes its original volume; when Carrol and Billie speak, one of the left-hand ones.

When Klaus and Franny speak, one of the left-hand sounds assumes a lower volume setting; when Errol speaks, one of the right-hand ones.

When Lana speaks, one of the right-hand sounds drops two settings below the original. When the volume set at this level descends below very soft, a silence results that should be punctuated by brief or very brief re-entries, very soft.

The sounds can vary in pitch or duration, but they vary especially in meaning: the name given them designates their form and origin, the sense they take on automatically in a context in which the same word appears, but there is not a single one of these sounds that cannot be used at times to describe water.

— breathing —
— animal movements —
— showers —

very loud, with the last notes of the carillon as five
o'clock strikes, loud, among the following lines:

— thunder —
— laughter —
— sighs —

above the abyss of elks and bears, the mass of the READER
river;

ALAN Dream.

the broken carcasses curve and cross in the abyss,

Dream.   BILLIE

which hurls itself to catch a thousand rainbows;

ANNOUNCER **The moon passes.**

low southward at the end of a branch,

The hour passes.

a pillar of water from the flexible flood bulges,

It was a dream.   CARROL

The month passes.

DINAH   Dream.

> *and the badgers hang by their tails, one would say, in the depths of the chasm,*

ERROL   Dream animals.

The season passes.

> *and become rounded in spirals in a fearful darkness,*

> Forest which dreams of forests   FRANNY
> which dream of animals which
> dream.

> *descend like a vast cylinder of air,*

ALAN   Bad dreams,

> *descend swept along by the current, then unroll . . .*

> burden of tomorrow.   BILLIE

> *—doors banging—*
> *—foghorns—*
> *—elevator machinery—*

loud, as six o'clock strikes, very loud

—flags flapping—
—breathing—
—animal movements—

October.

> *eagles rising in the east adorn the scene . . .*

> It's a dream.   CARROL

Autumn night.

DINAH   It was a dream.

> *rocks cut into forms of wild walnut trees . . .*

ERROL   Which stir around in a dream.

No longer completely night.

> *that of the pines of the snows . . .*

Which breathe and dream that they   FRANNY
sigh and dream.

*like the smoke of a vast forest fire at dawn which
rises above the trees . . .*

GEORGIA   Stirring around in his dream, fleeing from me there.

and glistens at dawn in whirlwinds of foam . . .

Tortured in her dream, pursuing   HENRY
me there.

in a sheet of snow and glistens . . .

Dawn.

the water splashes back up in all the colors,

ERROL   Muzzle of the morning.

striking the shaken rock,

Its claws.   FRANNY

then unrolls above the abyss, of darkness

Light that skims over the grass.

*curves and crosses at the point of leaving the
shore;*

Knife of the morning.   CARROL

a thousand rainbows;

DINAH   Its notches.

*the one falling toward the east of the flood like a
vast cylinder,*

Light that skims over the foundations of the rocks.

*a pillar of water descends in a fearful darkness,
one might say,*

ALAN   Chasm of the morning.

*bulges and becomes rounded fearful, one might
say.*

Its tolling.   BILLIE

GEORGIA   Scaffold of the morning.

in a darkness southward

Its forge.   HENRY

descends;

A reddening light.

a pillar of water toward the east

IGOR   Tomb of the morning.

which hurls itself,

Its decay.   JUDY

the one falling from the flood of darkness.

Heaving, breathing, murmuring, daybreak.

The mass of the river with all the colors, a thousand rainbows

First Parenthesis of OCTOBER

(Daybreak)

ALAN   Curls.

ERROL   Petals.

         Lashes.   BILLIE

         Nails.   CARROL

      at daybreak over the chaos of the waves, and READER
      glisten,

DINAH   Lips.

ANNOUNCER   **Cannas, dahlias in the solitude of early morning,**

      curve and cross in a sheet of embers with all its
      pines,

         Thorns.   FRANNY

starred with drops of fiery water in the double park,
cannas, dahlias.

ALAN   Cactus flowers.

     then unroll

         Bright salmon, yellow center. CARROL

         Orchid blossom.   BILLIE

     above the abyss

DINAH Old gold.

at the point of leaving the shore

ERROL Blackish garnet.

which hangs

Crimson with heliotrope underside. FRANNY

like a vast cylinder; striking the shaken rock, the water splashes back up.

ALAN Fiery red.

bulges and becomes rounded,

Persian lilac. BILLIE

hollow underneath southward in whirlwinds of foam,

Bluish mauve. CARROL

the mass of the river which hurls itself.

DINAH Violet with silvery tips.

An enormous rock, with all its pines over the chaos of waves which rise,

ERROL Deep sulphur yellow.

an enormous rock hollow underneath which hangs, juts out, between the two falls juts out,

Sulphur yellow striped and dotted FRANNY
with garnet.

like the smoke of a vast forest fire of about half a mile around between the two falls,

ALAN Vivid yellow.

in a horseshoe of a vast forest fire

Crimson lake. BILLIE

into two branches and curves,

ERROL Orange-colored fire glazed with yellow.

in a horseshoe of about half a mile around,

Pink mauve with a frill of madder FRANNY
red and gold.

the cataract divides like the smoke at the gaping
mouth of a chasm,

Salmon-colored old rose with rag- CARROL
ged petals.

and curve,

DINAH Purple violet.

rush in whirlwinds of foam which rise above the
trees,

ALAN Flesh-colored white.

whose hundred thousand torrents

Snow white. BILLIE

divide in two impetuous branches, striking the
shaken rock; the water splashes back up; it is less
a river than a sea

— whirlwinds of leaves —
— cameras clicking —
— turnstiles clicking —

fairly loud, as seven o'clock strikes, loud

> *— trees shivering —*
> *— doors banging —*
> *— foghorns —*

ANNOUNCER **It is the morning light.**

> *the cataract,*   READER

The hour of awakening.

> *with the result that at the very edge of the cascade*

The two cities shiver.

> *over the abyss,*

And all the hotels are stirring.

> *for a distance of almost six leagues,*

Those who have slept together for the first time.

ALAN Where are you?

> *the cataract,*

Where?   BILLIE

Those who have slept together for the first time in years.

Is it you, is it . . .   CARROL

steadily downward along a steep incline,

DINAH   Morning already of what year where?

Those who have slept together every night for years.

ERROL   Are we there?

a thousand rainbows curve and cross.

We, too, finally?   FRANNY

— laughter —
— sighs —
— birdcalls —

not too loud, as eight o'clock strikes, fairly loud

— diesel engines —
— whirlwinds of leaves —
— cameras clicking —

Those who have tried to vary their night by coming here.

GEORGIA   You are like him.

The river flows,

Who am I like?   HENRY

Those who did not think who would not have believed that they would sleep together here this night.

IGOR   Well, now . . .

divides,

What am I going to do now?   JUDY

Those who would have been happy to find here someone with whom they might sleep.

My hands rubbing the folds of the   KLAUS
sheets.

from Lake Erie all the way to the cataract,

Second Parenthesis of OCTOBER

(Departures)

NNOUNCER **In all the hotels, in all the motels,**

ALAN It's time.

like a pillar of water from the flood. READER

It's day, too. BILLIE

the taps of sinks and tubs, the heads of showers.

If we want to see the falls for a CARROL
last time . . .

It is that . . .

DINAH With all the suitcases to pack, we have time . . .

For so many couples in love, now it is time to face the road again.

ERROL We can hear cars leaving,

Into two branches and curves,

one following the other like drops FRANNY
in a fountain.

Those who had thought of staying here a few days more, but who now don't know.

GEORGIA Well?

what helps to make them so violent

But there are so many things we HENRY
haven't seen.

Those who only wanted to stay a weekend here and who are afraid to start back, who are afraid of what is waiting for them on their return.

IGOR However, we must . . .

in a fearful darkness,

We are already . . . JUDY

Those whose work obliges them to remain several days here, tortured, fascinated by the spectacle of this crowd of couples.

And I shall return tonight to the KLAUS
park in the midst of all those
murmurs and kisses.

but,

Here stepping from a car is a young woman alone.

LANA What have I come looking for here?

into a horseshoe of about half a mile around,

One by one cars leave the enormous parking lots, and newlyweds leaving pass others arriving.

ALAN We have to get away fairly fast.

One last look at the falls. BILLIE

their vertical height may be of about two hundred feet,

They must have traveled all night CARROL
long.

And old married couples leaving pass young ones arriving.

DINAH They didn't want to stop before they got to the falls,

the one falling to the east descends . . .

ALAN Do you think one day we, too, might be able to come back?

And the newlyweds leaving are sometimes astonished at the age of those arriving.

                           Perhaps one day we, too, will have   BILLIE
                           to come back,

                           having crossed Ohio,   CARROL

       are the falls . . .

ALAN crossing the state of New York,

Toward all the states the new couples scatter.

                           crossing Pennsylvania . . .   BILLIE

DINAH the Ontario . . .

       between the two falls juts out an enormous rock . . .

ALAN Farewell, Seagram Whiskey Tower.

Goat Island where so many couples stroll, the newlyweds, the revived, the united and the shattered.

                           Farewell, bell tower.   BILLIE

       at about nine miles from the latter lake,

—flags flapping—
—breathing—
—animal movements

fairly soft, as nine o'clock strikes, not too loud

> *— showers —*
> *— thunder —*
> *— laughter —*

> *with all the colors of the prism* . . . READER

LANA What is it that draws me here anyway?

ANNOUNCER **Since nine o'clock the two "Maids of the Mist" have begun passing each other in the gorge.**

> What is she doing alone? KLAUS

To make the boat trip from the American shore, you must first cross the park bridges, over the highways covered with departing automobiles,

> *Into the Ontario* . . .

climb some steps,

> *hollow underneath* . . .

put a quarter in the slot in the turnstile,

> *and empties* . . .

LANA   Where does he come from, alone? What city, what
country, what shore?

**pass over the wide crosswalk that leads to the iron-
and-glass tower,**

and glistens in the sun . . .

What confusion in those lovely eyes   KLAUS
almost hidden by her hair?

—birdcalls—
— trees shivering —
— doors banging —

soft, as ten o'clock strikes, fairly soft

—foghorns—
— elevator machinery —
— flags flapping —

go down in the transparent elevator.

LANA   What does he want with me? Why does he look at me,
alone in the middle of the crowd?

from Lake Erie . . .

**Down below, the path under the cliff leads to the lit-
tle building on the pier,**

which hangs,

**where you pay a dollar and a quarter for one of the
two "Maids of the Mist" which dock every twenty
minutes,**

GEORGIA   That young man alone in the middle of the crowd . . .

which springs from . . .

**the one American, the other Canadian, with their
flags.**

That young woman, so young, so   HENRY
beautiful, so lost; those eyes so lost,
so black, with that radiance . . .

of snow . . .

No need to get undressed, this time.

One would say she had lost every-   KLAUS
thing. Is she going to get on board
with us?

by the Niagara River . . .

**Specialists, estimating your height with a glance,
unhook a black waterproof that is supposed to come
down to your feet.**

LANA I don't see him anymore, he isn't looking at me anymore; it's better that way: I, too, am going to put on
this sooty cape to sail, almost a figure of darkness like
him, into this gloomy gorge.

with all its pines . . .

—sighs—
—diesel engines—
—whirlwinds of leaves—

very soft, as eleven o'clock strikes, soft

—cameras clicking—
—turnstiles clicking—
—birdcalls—

The penitents crowd into the little ship

GEORGIA I don't see him anymore.

It is formed . . .

I don't see her anymore.   HENRY

of white-painted metal,

I can't find her again, she is avoid-   KLAUS
ing me, is she even with us? Has
she even put on like us this bell of
darkness which cracks into stiff
folds?

Then unrolls in a sheet,

yellow smokestack, two lifeboats on the roof,

LANA Well-hidden in this hood.

over the chaos of the waves,

which coughs, groans, shakes, and departs.

Third Parenthesis of OCTOBER

(Moon Island)

GEORGIA I couldn't see you anymore.

What a face you're making! HENRY

at the point of leaving the shore. READER

ANNOUNCER **The pilot shut up in his cabin in the middle of the
ship of black penitents gives some details.**

IGOR It's as if we were leaving on a trip.

The mass of the river

But we really are on a trip. JUDY

The height of the American Falls is about 167 feet,

I would have liked to question her. KLAUS

bulges and becomes rounded like a vast cylinder

51 meters.

LANA Alone . . .

After having sailed along the American Falls,

which hurls itself,

GEORGIA Perhaps I should have come back here alone . . .

which hurls itself southward,

I shall come back here, I shall be   HENRY
alone before this long wall of
water.

whose ridge measures 1,075 feet,

IGOR   Where is she, what is she looking at, what is she
dreaming of?

bulges southward,

If only this water could wipe every-   JUDY
thing away.

327 meters,

Try to tear from her gently her   KLAUS
secret to deliver her from it.

the mass of the river,

you perceive up above,

LANA   If only someone could deliver me from my secret,
tear it from me very gently

*and becomes rounded like a vast cylinder the mass
of the river,*

on Moon Island,

GEORGIA   But if ever I had come back here alone . . .

at the point of leaving the shore,

Mangled, her old mangled body . . .   HENRY

leaning on the railing,

IGOR   To get rid of her, swallow up her up . . .

which hurls itself southward,

To be swallowed up . . .   JUDY

a young woman alone,

I hadn't seen that scarf rolled   KLAUS
around her neck.

then unrolls in a sheet of snow,

a young man watching her,

LANA   I fear my return has only restored my illusions, but
       what was I looking for?

bulges and becomes rounded like a vast cylinder,

a man no longer middle-aged with a girl in the mist,

GEORGIA   Since I have as much need of his hatred as of his love,
          of his contempt as of his attentions, how could I avoid
          it?

*and glistens in the sun with all the colors of the
prism at the point of leaving the shore, then unrolls,*

Oh, yes, I don't know, if she could   HENRY
change, if a bath could change
her . . .

**a young man near a lady who is probably not his
mother,**

IGOR   Wash myself entirely, wash myself of her and of me,
       wash myself.

*the one falling to the east in a sheet of snow and
glistens in the sun,*

Wash myself of him and of me,   JUDY
wash him.

old married couples white and black,

But now I see that she is with some-   KLAUS
one else, what was I thinking of?

*descends in a fearful darkness, one might say a
pillar of water from the flood,*

newlyweds of the day before,

LANA   I'm not going to be able to keep myself from follow-
       ing them, enticed by their radiance, and from imagin-
       ing that I, too . . .

*with all the colors of the prism the one falling to
the east descends; a thousand rainbows curve and
cross above the abyss,*

newlyweds of that morning.

GEORGIA To plunge into this glistening water, let myself be rolled and mangled . . .

in a fearful darkness, one might say a pillar of water from the flood;

I would have thought her lost, I HENRY would have thought I saw her rolling mangled, and then there she would be, but all changed.

They sail alongside The Bridal Veil.

IGOR No, days and days of intimacy; nights and nights more or less in hiding, and she will hate me . . .

a thousand rainbows curve and cross,

He who hates me already for what JUDY he's done to me, and it would be useless to try to make him believe . . .

They see the procession of yellow penitents descending the stairs of drenched wood to go back to the cave of the winds.

which rise above the trees;

But I won't be able to tell her, I KLAUS wouldn't even be able to tell her if she were the one, even if I see her.

over the abyss, striking the shaken rock, the water splashes back up in whirlwinds of foam,

The hour passes.

like the smoke of a vast forest fire,

LANA And if I ever found it again, that glance, and if even this time it were real, but it can't be real, and I would know very well this time not to believe in it.

low to catch in the abyss the broken carcasses of the elks and of the bears.

VIII

The Mists

Tracks A B: Skip the parentheses.

Tracks C E: Read "Rain."

Track D: Read "Rain" and "Viewmobile," but omit the lines of Morris, Lena and Karl.

Track F: Read "New Departures," "Rain" and "Viewmobile," omitting the lines of Morris and Lena.

Track G: Read "Rain," omitting Lena's lines.

Track H: Read "Autumn," "New Departures," "Rain" and "Viewmobile," omitting Lena's lines.

Track I: Read "Rain" and "Viewmobile."

Track J: Read everything.

in the center:

loud:

ANNOUNCER

fairly loud:

READER

at left:	at right:
not too loud:	not too loud:
GRACIE: old madam	HUGH: gigolo
fairly soft:	fairly soft:
IVO: vile seducer	JULIET: easy prey
MORRIS: widower	
soft:	
LENA: young woman alone	

very soft:

KARL: young man alone

Gracie, Hugh, Ivo and Juliet appear only in the parentheses.

If the right-hand channel is closed, Hugh can still be heard, but very softly; Juliet and Karl disappear.

If the left-hand channel is closed, Gracie can still be heard, but very softly; Ivo, Morris and Lena disappear.

Each person speaks as if he were alone; these are, however, dialogues between the deaf. The thoughts of Hugh reply to those of Gracie, not to the others; those of Juliet to those of Ivo. The solitude of the three others is more complete; they have never spoken a word to each other. Karl and Lena have only seen each other. Morris is with the dead.

Little Prelude for noon

In time with the first five notes of the Westminster carillon, loud, can be heard:

        in the middle:

at left:

           at right:

     fairly loud:

not too loud:

         fairly soft:

    — gust —

—brake screeching—

       —flag flapping —

    — train whistle —

      — elevator machinery —

—footsteps on damp rock —

      —foghorn—

   — police siren —

      — door slamming —

— rain —

     — animal movement —

—windowpane vibrating—

—diesel engine—

—snowstorm—

—whirlwind of a leaf—

—branch whispering—

—splashing—

When Karl speaks, one of the left-hand sounds resumes its original volume; when Lena or Morris
speaks, one of the right-hand sounds.

When Juliet speaks, one of the left-hand sounds assumes a lower volume setting; when Ivo speaks, one
of the right-hand sounds.

When Hugh speaks, one of the right-hand sounds
drops two settings below the original; when Gracie
speaks, one of the left-hand sounds drops two. Since
it takes a loud sound to cover a not too loud voice,
Hugh or Gracie can only be silenced when the ap-
propriate channel is closed.

—diesel engines—
—animal movements—
—doors slamming—

loud, with the last notes of the carillon as noon strikes,
fairly loud, among the following lines:

—foghorns—
—elevator machinery—
—flags flapping—

First Parenthesis of NOVEMBER

(The Canadian Falls)

ANNOUNCER **And they approach the Canadian Falls.**

southward becomes rounded in a vast cylinder,   READER

GRACIE But I sense that he is beside me in his black waterproof.

*then unrolls in a sheet of snow and glistens in the
sun with all the colors . . .*

But I sense that she has already   HUGH
found me again.

*Hang by their flexible tails at the end of a
branch . . .*

Their height is only 160 feet,

*The mass of the river which hurls itself southward
becomes rounded . . .*

49 meters.

*Descend in spirals to the depths of the chasm, and
badgers hurl themselves . . .*

IVO But for a while she belongs to me.

*Eagles swept along by the air current in a vast
cylinder . . .*

Then in a while he will get tired. JULIET

Then unroll cut into phantom forms . . .

The length of the crest is almost 2,100 feet,

*Adorn the scene, the mass of the river, wild wal-
nut trees, rocks in a sheet of snow,*

that is to say, 640 meters.

like the smoke of a vast forest fire of pines,

I would have to . . . KARL

which rises above the trees and glistens in the sun,

The day passes.

splashes back up in whirlwinds of foam

LENA I would have to . . .

over the chaos of the waves, with all these trees . . .

GRACIE His waterproof rubbing against my waterproof.

Striking the shaken rock, water with all the colors,

My chains rubbing against hers . . . HUGH

curves and crosses over the abyss

The month passes.

hollow underneath which hangs . . .

IVO For a while I won't let her escape.

A thousand rainbows . . .

And there I'll be, as before, JULIET
worse than before,

The one falling . . .

I don't know what I would have KARL
to do.

A pillar of water from the flood.

LENA I don't know what I would have to do, I would have
to . . .

An enormous rock, one would say, in the east . . .

OUNCER **The little steel ship juts out toward the interior of the immense caldron.**

in a fearful darkness juts out, descends,   READER

Soon they can no longer see even their own hands.

descends in a fearful darkness in the east, between the two falls;

They guess at the streaming face of their beloved under the black hood.

the one falling, one would say a pillar of all the colors of about half a mile around,

They don't talk anymore.

and glistens in the sun of water in a sheet of snow and curves in a horseshoe, then unrolls . . .

— rain —
— footsteps on damp rock —
— brakes screeching —

very loud, as one o'clock strikes, loud

— whirlwinds of leaves —
— diesel engines —
— animal movements —

In the tumult of luminous water,

From the flood, in a vast cylinder, divides in two branches, becomes rounded; a thousand arches southward . . .

a sublimated emerald.

The cataract which hurls itself; in the sky curves the mass of the river toward the gaping mouth of a chasm with all its pines over the chaos of the waves;

The depth in this place

and hollows over the abyss an enormous rock hollow underneath which hangs . . .

is 180 feet,

Whose hundred thousand torrents rush . . .

55 meters.

Juts out over the abyss,

—train whistles—
—gusts—
—branches whispering—

loud, as two o'clock strikes, very loud

—windowpanes vibrating—
—rain—
—footsteps on damp rock—

And the "Maid of the Mist" makes a horseshoe half turn,

in a horseshoe of about half a mile around between the two falls,

comes back under Goat Island.

it is less a river than an impetuous sea,

The Bridal Veil,

and curves, a thousand rainbows curve and cross;

Moon Island,

the cataract divides into two branches with the re-sult that at the very edge of the cascade, toward the gaping mouth of a chasm,

Second Parenthesis of NOVEMBER

(Autumn)

ANNOUNCER   **the American cataract.**

one would say a pillar of water from the flood   READER
whose hundred thousand torrents rush

November.

for a distance of almost six leagues, it is less a
river than an impetuous sea,

Conversations begin again.

in a fearful darkness; with the result that at the
very edge of the cascade,

GRACIE   The truth is that I have come back here too late.

steadily downward along a steep incline,

The truth is that it was too late   HUGH
in the season to come here.

for a distance of almost six leagues,

The splendor of the woods.

descends along a steep incline;

IVO   Of course, she's not the one I would have wanted, it's
another, and afterward I'll have to have another.

the river flows steadily downward,

And if ever someone else, someone JULIET
like him, suggests coming back . . .

in the east flows

Maples turning from ruby to garnet.

all the way to the cataract, from Lake Erie all the
way to the cataract the river . . .

The water, all that water, would KARL
have to . . .

Those falling so violent, it is that, from Lake
Erie,

In the fog.

what helps to make them with all the colors, but it is
that . . .

LENA All that water would have to . . .

Their vertical height may be of about two hundred
feet . . .

> *—flags flapping—*
> *—splashing—*
> *—snowstorms—*

fairly loud, as three o'clock strikes, loud

> *—police sirens—*
> *—train whistles—*
> *—gusts—*

ANNOUNCER **They stop at the Canadian pier,**

> *And glistens in the sun the falls so violent,*   READER

a few moments;

> *is found a sheet of snow*

a few black penitents get off,

> *into the Ontario at about nine miles from the lat-*
> *ter lake,*

others get on board.

Third Parenthesis of NOVEMBER

(New Departures)

what helps to make them . . .   READER

GRACIE Embittered, disgusted, exhausted, disappointed, we
must leave.

Then unrolls in . . .

ANNOUNCER **Sheets of fog.**

And empties . . .

It is high time to leave.   HUGH

But what

IVO Always another one, and each time it is the same dis-
gust.

springs from Lake Erie

Unable to resist, it will always   JULIET
be the same terror.

in a vast cylinder

Cold.

IVO Another one.

what helps to make them so violent,

Another one.   JULIET

All this water makes me give in   KARL
to this youth I never had.

the Niagara River, which hurls itself southward,
becomes rounded . . .

IVO   We have to go back.

Colder and colder.

they are formed by . . .

LENA   All this water . . .

It is high time to go back.   JULIET

—animal movements—
—doors slamming—
—foghorns—

not too loud, as four o'clock strikes, fairly loud

> *—elevator machinery—*
> *—flags flapping—*
> *—splashing—*

>> *it is that the mass of the river, from Lake Erie the*   READER
>> *mass of the river, all the way to the cataract, the*
>> *river which hurls itself southward, flows steadily,*

ANNOUNCER   **And they cross the river under the Rainbow Bridge,**

> *becomes rounded in a vast cylinder,*

finally to reach the American shore again,

> *downward,*

and turn in their shiny waterproofs.

> *then unrolls,*

Fourth Parenthesis of NOVEMBER

(Rain)

ANNOUNCER **From the other side of the metal-and-glass tower, a path**

along a steep incline, READER

and some steps lead under one of the ends of the American Falls.

in a sheet of snow and glistens in the sun

Freed for a moment from the clouds above the woods,

for a distance of almost six leagues

the sky,

with all the colors,

hidden the next moment in the tumult of rising wind,

with the result that at the very edge of the cascade,

sky glutted with rain,

the one falling to the east,

spectacle of the sky,

it is less a river than an impetuous sea,

trailing clouds,

descends in a fearful darkness,

rain,

whose hundred thousand torrents rush,

rain,

one would say a pillar of water from the flood,

rain,

toward the gaping mouth;

passes,

a thousand rainbows curve and cross over the abyss

the sky hollows out,

of a chasm,

clear.

the cataract

People have taken shelter in the souvenir shop.

divides

Flags, miniature toilets, hairbrushes, slides,

into two branches and curves

plates, pillows, decanters,

into a horseshoe of about

postcards, shirts, tapestries,

half a mile

ties, table napkins, ashtrays,

around between the two falls;

buttons, little naked porcelain women whose breasts come off to make salt and pepper shakers, bedlamps,

juts out an enormous rock

medallions of butterfly wings.

hollow underneath,

They go back up on the elevator.

which hangs

Fifth Parenthesis of NOVEMBER

(Viewmobile)

ANNOUNCER **Along the walks of the almost empty American park,**

with all its pines, READER

whirlwinds of leaves.

over the chaos of the waves.

The little train called the Viewmobile passes by,

The mass of the river

with a red diesel engine,

which hurls itself

with a whole assembly of old ladies

southward

who are to spend the night at Buffalo,

becomes rounded

crosses the first bridge,

in a vast cylinder,

negotiates Green Island,

then

crosses the second bridge,

unrolls

turns at Goat Island,

in a sheet

the stop for Moon Island,

of snow

—last rays of the red sun among the trees and waves—

and glistens

departs again,

           I would have to . . .   KARL

the stop for the cave of the winds,

LENA All this water . . .

departs again,

MORRIS I remember,

the stop for the Canadian Falls,

in the sun

departs again,

with all the colors

the stop for Three Sisters Islands,

          I see her tightening her scarf.   KARL

the calling home of the birds,

LENA I see him buttoning his raincoat.

night falls.

—footsteps on damp rock—
—brakes screeching—
—whirlwinds of leaves—

fairly soft, as five o'clock strikes, not too loud

—diesel engines—
—animal movements—
—doors slamming—

MORRIS She did so love these melancholy evenings at the falls.

ANNOUNCER **They are going away.**

                Go drink.   KARL

Fewer and fewer people.

LENA Go eat.

There are fewer couples especially.

MORRIS I certainly won't be able to sleep.

In the night,

                Go to sleep.   KARL

people alone,

LENA Go get warm.

young or old,

MORRIS   I remember.

in search of their phantoms,

Go to a dance hall perhaps.   KARL

their future companions

LENA   See a movie.

or those past.

—gusts—
—branches whispering—
—windowpanes vibrating—

soft, as six o'clock strikes, fairly soft

—rain—
—footsteps on damp rocks—
—brakes screeching—

MORRIS   Let the moon come.

The Viewmobile terminus.

Drag myself along these black paths.   KARL

Electric signs, all the damp windows.

LENA   Ramble along roads black with rain.

It is an almost dead city tonight.

MORRIS   The restaurant where we went is no longer there.

Few people in the streets.

Sit at a table in a bar waiting for   KARL
closing time.

The moon.

LENA   Buy a book perhaps and read in bed.

Clouds passing over the moon.

MORRIS   Let the wind come.

Empty parking lots.

This one is too gloomy, this one not   KARL
very clean, this one . . .

Doors creaking.

LENA   Waiting until it's time, but time for what?

> *— splashing —*
> *— snowstorms —*
> *— police sirens —*

very soft, as seven o'clock strikes, soft

> *— train whistles —*
> *— gusts —*
> *— branches whispering —*

Someone comes out of the movie.

MORRIS   They have all finally gone home to their cities, and I am alone among the trees and waters.

A shop window goes dark.

Scotch.   KARL

The mist rises from the gorge.

LENA   Have a Scotch maybe or a martini before dinner.

The moon through the mist.

MORRIS   It was the same cold breath rising, the same mist and the same moon, and we were alone in the middle of the park walking from isle to isle.

IX

The Phantoms

Tracks A B: Skip the parentheses.

Track C: Read "Christmas at Niagara," omitting the lines of Nelly, Milton, Liddy and Kent.

Track D: Read "Christmas at Niagara," omitting the lines of Milton, Liddy and Kent.

Track E: Read "Christmas at Niagara," omitting the lines of Liddy and Kent.

Track F: Read "New Floodlight Displays," omitting the lines of Nelly, Milton, Liddy and Kent; "Christmas at Niagara," omitting Kent's lines.

Track G: Read everything, but omit, in "New Floodlight Displays," the lines of Milton, Liddy and Kent.

Track H: Read everything, but omit, in "New Floodlight Displays," the lines of Liddy and Kent.

Track I: Read everything, but omit, in "New Floodlight Displays," Kent's lines.

Track J: Read everything.

If the right-hand channel is closed, Nelly can still be heard, but very softly, and Kent disappears.

If the left-hand channel is closed, Milton and Liddy disappear. But if it is only lowered, the voice of Milton will be heard as softly as that of Kent; that of Liddy will almost always be covered by the sound effects.

If the right-hand channel is lowered, Kent can be rendered practically inaudible, still covered by the sound effects, and Nelly can be brought to the center where she is heard even more softly than Liddy.

Little Prelude for eight o'clock in the evening.

In time with the four first notes of the Westminster carillon, fairly loud, can be heard:

        in the center:

to the left: to the right:

        not too loud:

fairly soft:

            soft:

      —automobile in snow—

           —brakes screeching—

—car door being slammed—

           —footsteps on damp rock—

       —footsteps in snow—

          —rain—

—branch snapping—

           —windowpane vibrating—

—creaking—

           —branch whispering—

        —icicle falling—

           —diesel engine—

—heart beating—

—gust—

—tree shivering—

—snowstorm—

—Christmas chorale Von Himmel hoch *on the organ—*

When Kent speaks, one of the left-hand sounds resumes its initial volume; when Liddy speaks, one of the right-hand sounds.

When Milton speaks, one of the right-hand sounds resumes a volume setting lower than the original; when Nelly speaks, one of the left-hand sounds.

And when the Reader speaks, one of the right-hand sounds drops two settings lower than the original.

—diesel engines—
—branches whispering—
—windowpanes vibrating—

fairly loud, with the last notes of the carillon as eight
o'clock strikes, not too loud, among the following lines:

—rain—
—footsteps on damp rocks—
—brakes screeching—

ANNOUNCER **Phantoms.**

Bears, bears, and bears   READER

The hour passes

and elks, elks and, in the abyss, the broken car-
casses . . .

with its phantoms.

to catch in the abyss the broken carcasses, low to
catch

The night passes

—branches snapping—
—car doors being slammed—
—snowstorms—

loud, as nine o'clock strikes, fairly loud, even before
the strokes of eight o'clock have ended

—*gusts*—
—*diesel engines*—
—*branches whispering*—

> *at the end of a low branch by their flexible tails at
> the end of a branch,*

with its demons.

> *low to catch in the abyss the broken carcasses, hang*

The month passes

> *by their flexible tails, badgers hang*

with its stale smells and echos.

> *in the depths of the abyss and by their flexible tails
> at the end of a branch,*

First Parenthesis of DECEMBER

(New Floodlight Displays)

ANNOUNCER **During the month of December the floodlight displays began at 8:30 P.M.**

descend in spirals the badgers swept along by the air current READER

Snow white. KENT

and the eagles hang, adorn the scene;

LIDDY Flesh-colored white.

in the depths of the abyss, rocks cut into phantom forms,

MILTON Purple violet.

wild walnut trees, badgers, pines, swept along by the air current,

Salmon-colored old rose with ragged petals. NELLY

like the smoke of a vast forest fire of eagles above the trees . . .

In the midst of the fogs.

And the water splashes back up in whirlwinds of foam . . .

Rosy mauve with a frill of mad- KENT
der red and gold.

Eagles swept along by the air current, striking the
shaken rock descend in spirals;

LIDDY Orange-colored fire glazed with yellow.

The water splashes back up in the depths of the
chasm in whirlwinds,

MILTON Crimson lake.

in the depths of the chasm of foam,

Vivid yellow. NELLY

and the badgers descending in spirals,

In the midst of the frost.

rise, hang above the trees,

Sulphur yellow striped and dot- KENT
ted with garnet.

by their flexible tails like the smoke of a vast forest
fire of pines swept along by the air current . . .

LIDDY Deep sulphur yellow.

Wild walnut trees at the end of the rocks . . .

MILTON Violet with silvery tips.

Branches cut into phantom forms adorn the scene
of eagles,

Bluish mauve. NELLY

adorn the low scene of eagles swept along by the
current,

In the falling snow.

to catch in the abyss of air the rocks cut into
phantom form . . .

Persian lilac. KENT

Descend in spirals the broken carcasses of elks to
the depths of the chasm,

LIDDY Fiery red.

and of bears and badgers, of pines, of wild wal-
nut trees,

MILTON Crimson, with heliotrope underside.

hang the bears by their tails,

Blackish garnet.   NELLY

and flexible like the smoke of a vast forest fire,

At eleven o'clock the floodlight displays will end.

at the end of a low branch, the broken carcasses of
the elks, to catch in the abyss,

—trees shivering—
—hearts beating—
—groans—

very loud, as ten o'clock strikes, loud

> *—creaking—*
> *—branches snapping—*
> *—car doors being slammed—*

> Black.   KENT

> to catch in the abyss the broken carcasses of the elks   READER
> and of the bears which rise above the trees . . .

LIDDY   Black.

> *at the end of a low branch, the water splashes*
> *back up in whirlwinds of foam,*

> > *—Christmas chorale* Von Himmel
> > hoch *played on the organ—*
> > *—icicles falling—*
> > *—footsteps in snow—*

loud, as eleven o'clock strikes, very loud, even before
the strokes of ten o'clock have ended

—automobiles in snow—
—trees shivering—
—hearts beating—

MILTON   Black.

flexible over the abyss striking the shaken rock,

Black.   NELLY

by their tails curve and cross;

Second Parenthesis of DECEMBER

(Christmas at Niagara)

NOUNCER **Everywhere immense Christmas trees covered with multicolored garlands.**

hang a thousand rainbows,   READER

And I go back into the black night. KENT

and badgers in the east descend in a fearful darkness, one would say a pillar of water from the flood,

LIDDY And I lock myself up in my own black night.

they are falling to the depths of the chasm,

Masses in the churches with illuminated stained-glass windows.

with all the colors,

MILTON With her before, but it was in another season.

descend in spirals in a sheet of snow and glisten in the moonlight,

With him before in this snow. NELLY

swept along by the air current which hurls itself southward,

I hate this night.   KENT

becomes rounded in a vast cylinder,

**Christmas parties in all the restaurants decorated
with mistletoe and holly.**

then unroll

LIDDY   I hate this night.

*the eagles over the chaos of the waves, the mass of
the river,*

MILTON   I hate all these new sounds which push her back into
her darkness, into her oblivion.

*an island hollow underneath which hangs with all
its trees,*

How he would have loved all these   NELLY
new sounds which help me to draw
him back from the darkness!

juts out

The dance.

between the two falls;

The night.

*the cataract divides into two branches and curves
into a horseshoe,*

MILTON   Struggling among other phantoms.

at the gaping mouth of a chasm,

Splashing up from the waters,   NELLY
sweeping me along.

*it is less a river than an impetuous sea whose hun-
dred thousand torrents rush,*

LIDDY   Rush me.

with the result that at the very edge of the cascade,

MILTON   Swimming, she who in her whole life never swam, her
head emerging from the waters of oblivion, her hair
spreading out, immense . . .

for a distance of almost six leagues,

A spring, let me drink there, NELLY
here in this room where I am
alone listening to the false sounds
of Christmas . . .

downward along a steep incline

The dancers grow tired.

the river flows steadily

Drifting blocks of ice,

all the way to the cataract,

crossing bridges of ice.

from Lake Erie,

The churches close.

it is that . . .

LIDDY I give up.

But what helps to make them so violent . . .

Couples come undone.

Their vertical height may be of about two hundred feet.

LIDDY I won't be able to sleep here tonight; I must flee over
the icy roads.

At about nine miles from the latter lake are the falls . . .

MILTON Rolls, rolls me in its sleep and in its rain and in its
snow and in its hail and in its icefield which burns
me . . .

And empties into the Ontario . . .

And splashes back up a great win- NELLY
ter smoke which rolls me and
pierces me and kneads me in a
whole round dance of other phan-

toms. Oh, if only I were alone with him!

The lights go out.

LIDDY Farewell.

—branches whispering—
—windowpanes vibrating—
—rain—

fairly loud, as midnight strikes, loud

> *—footsteps on damp rocks—*
> *—brakes screeching—*
> *—Christmas chorale* Von Himmel
> hoch *played on the organ—*

OUNCER **Some single people on the snow. What are they doing on the road at this frozen hour?**

MILTON Sleep.

A few staggering pedestrians.

> Sleep. NELLY

> *—car doors being slammed—*
> *—snowstorms—*
> *—gusts—*

not too loud, as one o'clock strikes, fairly loud, even before the strokes of midnight have ended

—diesel engines—
—branches whispering—
—windowpanes vibrating—

Footprints.

In a frost of tears.   NELLY

The single people

MILTON   Tears splashing back up in a whirlwind.

clutching their sheets.

In a haze of tears.   NELLY

— hearts beating —
— groans —
— creaking —

fairly soft, as two o'clock strikes, not too loud

> *— branches snapping —*
> *— car doors slamming —*
> *— snowstorms —*

Here is one getting up

MILTON   I'm thirsty.

He goes to the window.

I hear him going to the window.   NELLY

He looks out.

MILTON   What desolation!

He sighs,

He is thirsty.   NELLY

— icicles falling —
— footsteps in snow —
— automobiles in snow —

soft, as three o'clock strikes, fairly soft

— trees shivering —
— hearts beating —
— groans —

shivers,

MILTON   Would anyone ever believe there were hotels here, churches, parties, anything beyond this room floating in whirlwinds of snow?

totters,

I can do nothing for him.   NELLY

he sees something approaching outside the window,

MILTON   Come!

it is nothing,

It is a gust of tears.   NELLY

—rain—
—footsteps on damp rock—
—brakes screeching—

very soft, as four o'clock strikes, soft

> *—Christmas   chorale* Von Himmel
>   hoch *played on the organ—*
> *—icicles falling—*
> *—footsteps in snow—*

which springs from Lake Erie . . .   READER

he puts his hands before his eyes,

MILTON   What did I see?

he comes slowly back toward his bed,

A whole cataract of tears.   NELLY

It is formed by the Niagara River . . .

**he sits down and remains motionless on his bed for a
long time in the night listening to the wind.**

X

The Styx

Tracks A B: Skip the parentheses.

Track C: Read "The Little Cat," but omit the lines of Otto, Nadia, Morgan.

Track D: Read "The Little Cat," omitting the lines of Nadia and Morgan, and "Lectures."

Track E: Read "The Little Cat," omitting Morgan's lines, "Lectures" and "Bobby Leach and Charles Stephens," omitting the lines of Albert, Bella, Charlton, Doris, Ernest and Flannery.

Track F: Read "The Little Cat," "Lectures," "Bobby Leach and Charles Stephens," omitting the lines of Albert, Bella, Charlton and Doris, and "George Stathakis and Jean Laussier," omitting the lines of Albert, Bella, Charlton, Doris, Ernest and Flannery.

Track G: Read everything, but omit, in "Bobby Leach and Charles Stephens," the lines of Albert and Bella, in "George Stathakis and Jean Laussier," those of Albert, Bella, Charlton and Doris, and in "The Gallant Snow," those of Albert, Bella, Charlton, Doris, Ernest and Flannery.

Track H: Read everything, but omit, in "George Stathakis and Jean Laussier," the lines of Albert and Bella, in "The Gallant Snow," those of Albert, Bella, Charlton and Doris.

Track I : Read everything, but omit, in "The Gallant Snow," the lines of Albert and Bella.

Track J : Read everything.

If the right-hand channel is closed, Ernest and Flannery can still be heard, but very softly; Otto, Albert, Bella and Nadia disappear.

If the left-hand channel is closed, Grace and Horace can still be heard, but softly; Charlton, Doris and Morgan disappear.

The four couples, who appear only in the parentheses, speak now aloud even though softly.

Second Little Prelude for five o'clock in the morning.

In time with the first three notes of the Westminster carillon, not too loud, can be heard:

        in the center:

at left:

            at right:

      fairly soft:

soft:

         very soft:

     —eagle's cry—

         —car door being slammed—

—crowd—

         —branch snapping—

—drop of water—

        —creaking—

—dance music—

        —groan—

    —badger's cry—

        —heart beating—

—deep sigh—

—tree shivering—

—panting—

—snowstorm—

—turnstile clicking—

—automobile in snow—

—police siren—

—Christmas chorale Von Himmel
hoch *played on the organ—*

—crunching—

For the repetitions of the chorale, *Von Himmel hoch,* it will be wise to use some of the numerous variations this theme has inspired in famous composers.

When Otto, Nadia and Morgan speak, one of the sounds from the other side resumes its original volume; when Grace, Horace, Ernest, Flannery, Charlton, Doris, Albert and Bella speak, one of the sounds of the other side assumes a volume setting lower than the original.

When the Reader speaks, one of the left-hand sounds drops two settings below the original; when it is the Announcer, one of the right-hand ones.

—trees shivering—
—hearts beating—
—groans—

not too loud, with the last notes of the carillon as five
o'clock strikes, fairly soft, among the following lines:

> *—creaking—*
> *—branches whispering—*
> *—car doors being slammed—*

ANNOUNCER **The hour passes.**

> *Bears from the flood,*   READER

MORGAN White in the white night.

The scene of phantoms is ready for other forms.

> *and a pillar of water, the cataract,*

> White in the white night.   NADIA

> *the broken carcasses of the elks . . .*

The night passes.

> White.   OTTO

> *divides into two branches, one would say . . .*

Here is the procession of barrels.

In the abyss, in a fearful darkness . . .

    — crowds —
    — Christmas chorale Von Himmel
    hoch *played on the organ —*
    — automobiles in snow —

fairly loud, as six o'clock strikes, not too loud

— snowstorms —
— trees shivering —
— hearts beating —

The month passes.

MORGAN   Who?

    to catch . . .

        What? Who?   NADIA

    descends and curves . . .

        Why?   OTTO

    *at the end of a low branch in a horseshoe to the
east . . .*

MORGAN   Who would dare?

    and badgers hang by their flexible tails . . .

        But what man would pass through NADIA
        this window on the Styx?

    The one falling

        In the white night.   OTTO

First Parenthesis of JANUARY

(The Little Cat)

ANNOUNCER **At the beginning of October, 1901, a schoolteacher, Mrs. Anna Edson Taylor . . .**

in the depths of the chasm with all the colors. READER

MORGAN Of the white night.

Between two falls descend in spirals,

In the night who? NADIA

jut out in the moonlight swept along by the air current

One would say barrels. OTTO

and glisten,

MORGAN In the white night a mad foam.

eagles of snow.

The season passes.

An island hollow underneath adorns the scene which hangs with all its trees . . .

Mrs. Anna Edson Taylor strokes a little cat.

Then unrolls in a sheet of phantoms . . .

Mewing in the white night. NADIA

In a vast cylinder . . .

Mrs. Anna Edson Taylor inserts her little cat into a vast barrel,

Cut into form and becomes rounded . . .

and throws it.

Over the chaos of the waves, the pines, the wild walnut trees, the rocks . . .

It fell into the Canadian Falls.

The mass of the river which hurls itself southward . . .

When they fished out the barrel, the little cat was dead.

MORGAN   Cats' eyes in the white night.

The barrel itself was intact.

Like the smoke of a vast forest fire, the mass of the river . . .

The years pass.

Above the trees,

           Snows and snows.   NADIA

over the chaos of the waves,

           Black in the white night.   OTTO

—panting—
—deep sighs—
—dance music—

loud, as seven o'clock strikes, fairly loud

> *—drops of water—*
> *—crowds—*
> *—Christmas chorale* Von Himmel
> hoch *played on the organ—*

ANNOUNCER   **On the morning of October 4, 1901, Mrs. Anna Edson Taylor stepped into her barrel.**

> *which hurls itself southward,*   READER

It was like a whiskey barrel not quite so tall as she,

> *which rises,*

of wood bound in steel.

> *becomes rounded.*

In white letters, the legend "Queen of the Mist."

> Drunk with a different desert, mad   NADIA
> with a different time, if only I
> could, myself, make my way with
> him to that island.

> *An island hollow underneath which hangs with
> all its trees . . .*

MORGAN   Liquor of the dead.

She had fastened to the bottom of the barrel a little blacksmith's anvil to serve as a keel.

Striking the shaken rock, the water splashes back up in whirlwinds of foam . . .

A vehicle in the form of a coffin to   NADIA
force the door of the dead.

She had the top firmly closed, and let herself be put into the upper rapids in order to be hurled toward the Canadian Falls.

Juts out over the abyss . . .

Rolled in the barrel of my room,   OTTO
alone, all the walls, all the sheets
dripping tears of the bitter wine of
the dead, I approach this door of
gaping fog . . .

In a horseshoe between the two falls . . .

Where the dawn is breaking.   NADIA

—badgers' cries—
—eagles' cries—
—police sirens—

very loud, as eight o'clock strikes, loud

—turnstiles clicking—
—panting—
—deep sighs—

The setting of the frost at dawn.

MORGAN   Hammers of frost, hammers of dawn.

The Canadian ship, "Maid of the Mist," fished out the Queen of the Mist in her barrel.

Like a vast cylinder . . .

Dawn comes up.

A thousand rainbows curve and cross.

Pale.   NADIA

Say, what did she see? Say!   OTTO

She bleeds.   NADIA

Second Parenthesis of JANUARY

(Lectures)

ANNOUNCER	**Mrs. Anna Edson Taylor then made a lecture tour to tell about her adventure.**
MORGAN	Say, what did you see?

She is silent.	NADIA
She always tells the same thing.	OTTO
She tells nothing.	NADIA

MORGAN She is silent.

She found the door closed.	NADIA
She rolled alongside the door.	OTTO
She has forgotten.	NADIA

MORGAN She is forgotten.

She rolled in oblivion.	NADIA
She rolls.	OTTO
She shows herself.	NADIA

MORGAN She shows her wrinkles and scars.

She shows her eyes already dead.	NADIA

How much will you pay to see OTTO
the eyes of oblivion?

Her eyes of a dead cat rolled NADIA
by the torrent.

—creaking—
—branches snapping—
—car doors being slammed—

loud, as nine o'clock strikes, very loud

> *—crunching—*
> *—badgers' cries—*
> *—eagles' cries—*

ANNOUNCER   **Dawn reveals some cautious automobiles on the roads.**

> *Then unrolls in a sheet of snow . . .*   READER

Some clouds and gusts pass.

> *And curves a pillar of water from the flood . . .*

Third Parenthesis of JANUARY

> (Bobby Leach and Charles Stephens)

| | everything okay? | ALBERT |

The cataract divides into two branches in a fear-ful darkness, one might say, toward the gaping mouth of a chasm. READER

everything's okay. BELLA

ANNOUNCER **On July 25, 1911, a little Englishman, Bobby Leach,**

Not too tired? ALBERT

in the east, whose torrents rush and glisten . . .

everything's okay. BELLA

CHARLTON Everything has changed.

We're getting there. ALBERT

DORIS We have changed.

We have plenty of time. BELLA

went over the Canadian Falls in a steel cylinder.

everything okay? ALBERT

The one falling toward the sun; it is less a river than a sea with all the colors . . .

He had to spend twenty-three weeks in a hospital, with his knees broken and his jaw shattered.

MORGAN Say, what did he hear?

          Absurd, in the white light of NADIA
          summer.

          Winter. ALBERT

          Be quiet, let him speak; he's OTTO
          still speaking.

          Winter. BELLA

          I didn't hear well, he didn't NADIA
          hear well, he's going to begin
          again, I think.

       And at the very edge of the cascade, glistens in the sun,

Died during a visit to New Zealand from slipping on an orange peel.

MORGAN Tell him . . .

          Tell him that . . . NADIA

          Tell him this time that . . . OTTO

          Find him this time, tell him . . . NADIA

Winter landscape.

       with all the colors . . .

          White. ALBERT

          Soft. ERNEST

CHARLTON After the flood.

          White. BELLA

          Flesh-colored. FLANNERY

       Then unrolls in a sheet of snow and the one falling to the east descends in a fearful darkness,

DORIS It was before the war.

becomes rounded in a vast cylinder,

What time is it? BELLA

one would say a pillar of water from the flood,

Are you hungry? ALBERT

In 1930, Charles Stephens, an Englishman, father of eleven children, went over the falls in a barrel.

Hungry? BELLA

MORGAN Tell him . . .

Aren't you hungry? ALBERT

the mass of the river which hurls itself southward,

everything's okay. BELLA

Cry out to him . . . NADIA

one would say a pillar of water from the flood,

They found only one of his arms, torn off.

over the chaos of the waves . . .

Brilliant velvety amaranth with ERNEST
silvery flecks.

Fourth Parenthesis of JANUARY

(George Stathakis and Jean Laussier)

ANNOUNCER **Couples walk in the snowy landscape among the rocks and crags.**

I think I . . .   ALBERT

Are you very hungry?   BELLA

My fine, my beautiful purplish   FLANNERY
red tinged with garnet shaded
with maroon.

The one falling to the east descends in a fear-   READER
ful darkness . . .

CHARLTON   The bridge collapsed five years later.

What about you?   ALBERT

DORIS   After thirty years we have come back.

I don't know.   BELLA

On July 5, 1930, George Stathakis in a big barrel,

Say . . .   OTTO

What's the matter?   NADIA

held back behind the Canadian Falls for fourteen

hours, died of asphyxiation and only his body went over the falls.

MORGAN Say . . .

What did you see? NADIA

What city glimpsed? OTTO

What island? NADIA

Hollow underneath which hangs with all its trees,
and glistens in the sun with all the colors,

MORGAN In the middle of summer.

In the middle of winter.

Copper yellow. ERNEST

White. NADIA

Tawny sepals. FLANNERY

White. OTTO

CHARLTON That enormous tower that looks like a castle of water didn't use to be there.

Everything okay? ALBERT

Bronze. ERNEST

MORGAN White.

I don't know. BELLA

DORIS That little belfry with the carillon wasn't there.

Dark, purplish, velvety. FLANNERY

White. NADIA

Finally, Jean Laussier, in an enormous rubber balloon,

We ate a lot yesterday. ALBERT

Between the two falls juts out an island of snow . . .

And then . . . BELLA

went over the Canadian Falls without the least harm.

> *— snowstorms —*
> *— trees shivering —*
> *— hearts beating —*

fairly loud, as ten o'clock strikes, loud

— groans —
— creaking —
— branches snapping —

MORGAN Snow

> *And curves into a horseshoe then unrolls in a*   READER
> *sheet . . .*

           Of snow.   NADIA

> *The cataract*

— drops of water —
— crowds —
— Christmas chorale Von Himmel hoch *played on the
organ —*

not too loud, as eleven o'clock strikes, fairly loud

> *— automobiles in snow —*
> *— snowstorms —*
> *— trees shivering —*

NOUNCER **The Viewmobile isn't running anymore.**

divides into two branches,

The snow.   OTTO

becomes rounded in a vast cylinder

Snow in mourning.   NADIA

whose torrents rush toward the gaping mouth of a
chasm.

—turnstiles clicking—
—panting—
—deep sighs—

fairly soft, as noon strikes, not too loud, even before
the strokes of eleven o'clock have ended

—dance music—
—drops of water—
—crowds—

The two "Maids of the Mist" are lined up side by
side on the Canadian shore.

MORGAN   Snow wedding.

The mass of the river which hurls itself south-
ward,

In the snow.   NADIA

The bridge leading to the elevator tower is closed.

Covered with snow.   OTTO

it is less a river than a sea . . .

Snow foam.   NADIA

—crunching—
—badgers' cries—
—eagles' cries—

soft, as one o'clock strikes, fairly soft, before even the
strokes of noon have ended

—police sirens—
—turnstiles clicking—
—panting—

The cave of the winds is closed.

MORGAN   Gusts of snow.

> *Over the chaos of the waves.*

> > Snow whirlwinds.   NADIA

> > *—groans—*
> > *—creaking—*
> > *—branches snapping—*

very soft, as two o'clock strikes, soft

—car doors being slammed—
—crunching—
—badgers' cries—

The Canadian tunnel is closed.

> *And at the edge of the cascade . . .*

> > Snow forest.   OTTO

> *Which hangs with all its trees . . .*

But all the souvenir shops are open.

> *The river flows steadily downward along a steep incline for a distance of almost six leagues,*

Fifth Parenthesis of JANUARY

(The Gallant Snow)

ANNOUNCER **A few couples.**

GRACE It is ugly, I agree with you, it is ugly, it is ridiculous, all these fools gaping at that flowing water . . .

A few kisses.

from Lake Erie all the way to the cataract . . . READER

CHARLTON Nor that elevator with its iron-and-glass cage on the other bank.

Sprung from a hardy crimson bud. ERNEST

HORACE But I told you perfectly clearly that I didn't want to come here.

Lusterless. FLANNERY

The cataract divides into two branches,

A few caresses.

and curves

A few sighs.

There is the emotion, too. ALBERT

DORIS Was that wax museum, "Madame Tussaud's," there?

into a horseshoe . . .

A few automobiles going away.

Watch out! BELLA

MORGAN Farewell.

It is that . . .

Chunks of ice fall from the trees.

but what helps to make them so violent . . .

GRACE Yes, I know that, my pet, don't get mad, pet.

Their height . . .

Shaded with dark garnet. ERNEST

Vertical . . .

Veined. FLANNERY

Perhaps . . .

HARLTON I can't remember.

Of about two hundred feet . . .

HORACE You asked me to drive you here; I have driven you.

*In the Ontario at about nine miles from the latter
lake are the falls.*

DORIS We've seen "Madame Tussaud's" since then in London.

*They are formed by the Niagara River which
springs from Lake Erie and empties . . .*

XI

The Cold

Tracks A B: Skip the parentheses.

Track C: Read "Wax Figures," but omit the lines of Enoch, Felicia, Gina, Helmut, Ivor and Judy.

Track D: Read "The Photograph" and "Wax Figures," omitting the lines of Enoch, Felicia, Gina, Helmut, Ivor and Judy.

Track E: Read everything, but omit, in the parentheses, the lines of Anthony, Barbara, Claudius, Dollie, Enoch, Felicia, Gina, Helmut, Ivor and Judy.

Track F: Read everything, but omit, in the parentheses, the lines of Anthony, Barbara, Claudius, Dollie, Enoch, Felicia, Gina and Helmut.

Track G: Read everything, but omit, in the parentheses, the lines of Anthony, Barbara, Claudius, Dollie, Enoch and Felicia.

Track H: Read everything, but omit, in the parentheses, the lines of Anthony, Barbara, Claudius and Dollie.

Track I: Read everything, but omit, in the parentheses, the lines of Anthony and Barbara.

Track J: Read everything.

in the center:

loud:

ANNOUNCER

at left: at right:

fairly loud:

IVOR: vile seducer   JUDY: easy prey

READER

not too loud:

GINA: old madam   KENNY: young man alone

HELMUT: gigolo

fairly soft:

PEGGY: Negro   ENOCH and FELICIA: Negro
widow   gardeners

soft:

CLAUDIUS and DOLLIE: old married couple

OSCAR: Negro widower

very soft:

NORA: widow   ANTHONY and BARBARA: "just-
marrieds"

If the right-hand channel is closed, Judy can still be heard, but softly; Kenny, but very softly; Enoch, Felicia, Oscar, Anthony and Barbara disappear.

If the left-hand channel is closed, Ivor can still be heard, but softly; Gina and Helmut, but very softly; Peggy, Claudius, Dollie and Nora disappear.

Gina, Helmut, Enoch, Felicia and Kenny appear only in the parentheses.

The couples speak aloud, even if it is very softly, and the isolated characters talk to themselves, even if the volume is set for not too loudly.

Little Prelude for three o'clock

In time with the first two notes of the Westminster carillon, fairly soft, can be heard:

      in the center:

at left:

          at right:

    soft:

very soft:

          not too loud:

   — mewing —

       — crowd —

— car door being opened —

        — drop of water —

— buzzing —

       — dance music —

— brass band —

       — deep sigh —

— sob —

       — panting —

       — turnstile clicking —

—grunting—

    —police siren—

—camera clicking—

    —automobile in snow—

—train whistle—

    —badger's cry—

—icicle falling—

    —crunching—

   —police whistle—

When one of the characters speaks, one of the sounds on the other side resumes its original volume.

When the Reader speaks, one of the right-hand sounds assumes a lower volume setting than the original; when it is the Announcer, one of the left-hand sounds.

These sounds never cover the voice of the Announcer or the Reader but only interfere with it. If one of the channels is silenced, one or the other voice can then be found again in its purity.

—turnstiles clicking—
—panting—
—deep sighs—

fairly soft, among the last notes of the carillon as three o'clock strikes, soft

—dance music—
—drops of water—
—crowds—

ANNOUNCER **A few couples in the night.**

—crunching—
—badgers' cries—
—automobiles in snow—

not too loud, as four o'clock strikes, fairly soft, even before the strokes of three o'clock and the carillon have ended

—police sirens—
—turnstiles clicking—
—panting—

PEGGY **In the night snow.**

—sobs—
—brass bands—
—buzzing—

fairly loud, as five o'clock strikes, not too loud, even
before the strokes of four o'clock and the carillon have
ended

> *— car doors being opened —*
> *— crunching —*
> *— badgers' cries —*

NORA   In the snow.

> In the night.   OSCAR

> *— icicles falling —*
> *— train whistles —*
> *— cameras clicking —*

loud, as six o'clock strikes, fairly loud, even before the
strokes of five o'clock and the carillon have ended

— grunting —
— sobs —
— brass bands —

First Parenthesis of FEBRUARY

(Blondin)

ANNOUNCER **The hour passes.**

Eagles swept along by the air current READER

In 1859, Jean-François Gravelet, called Blondin . . .

descend in spirals to the depths of the chasm,

The day passes.

and badgers hang by their flexible tails,

Crossed the gorge on a high wire . . .

at the end of a low branch,

The month passes.

to catch in the abyss,

Jumped on the wire, ran on the wire, made perilous leaps on the wire . . .

the broken carcasses of the elks and of the bears.

The years pass.

Rocks cut into phantom forms adorn the scene from Lake Erie all the way to the cascade . . .

Walked backward on the wire, sat down on the wire, lay down on the wire . . .

The one falling to the east descends in a fearful darkness . . .

Night falls.

The river runs on along a steep incline . . .

Walked on the wire with baskets tied to his feet, walked on the wire with stilts.

Pines, wild walnut trees . . .

NORA Covered with snow.

And at the edge of the cascade, it is less a river, one would say, than a sea whose torrents rush like the smoke of a vast forest fire toward the gaping mouth of a chasm . . .

In 1860, Jean-François Gravelet, called Blondin, came back to the falls.

A pillar of water from the flood toward the gaping mouth of a chasm splashes back up in whirl-winds of foam which rise above the trees . . .

Covered with snow.   OSCAR

It was in the presence of the Prince of Wales.

Rush . . .

PEGGY What?

A thousand torrents . . .

NORA What is he saying?

Striking the shaken rock the water . . .

Striped.   ENOCH

A few dim lights in the night.

Orange shaded with lavender FELICIA
changing to lavender pink, very
erect stem.

It is less a river than a sea whose arches, at the edge of the cascade, curve and cross over the abyss . . .

GINA   It is because I wanted to see you here.

PEGGY   What's it all about?

On his tightrope, Jean-François Gravelet, called Blondin, waved his hat, and John Travis, a crack shot, aboard the "Maid of the Mist," put a bullet through it.

HELMUT   And now you don't like it anymore.

The river runs on along a steep incline and in the sky curves . . .

On his tightrope, Jean-François Gravelet, called Blondin, lowered a pitcher at the end of a rope to the "Maid of the Mist," had it filled by the crew, pulled it up again and drank of the water of the abyss.

Thirst.   OSCAR

Emotion.   ANTHONY

From Lake Erie all the way to the cascade in the sky and cross . . .

PEGGY   Thirst.

They are young newlyweds, too.   BARBARA

A thousand arches over the abyss . . .

Hunger.   OSCAR

NORA   Thirst.

One would say a pillar of water from the flood . . .

PEGGY   Hunger.

On his tightrope, Jean-François Gravelet, called Blondin, cooked himself an omelette on a little stove and treated himself to it.

In the past.   OSCAR

NORA In the cold.

> *— drops of water —*
> *— crowds —*
> *— police whistles —*

very loud, as seven o'clock strikes, loud

> *— mewing —*
> *— icicles falling —*
> *— train whistles —*

PEGGY All this is very old.

NORA In the night.

ANNOUNCER **On the counters can be seen tapestries with water-falls . . .**

CLAUDIUS I saw only you.

> *— police sirens —*
> *— turnstiles clicking —*
> *— panting —*

loud, as eight o'clock strikes, very loud, even before the strokes of seven o'clock have ended

> *— deep sighs —*
> *— dance music —*
> *— drops of water —*

In the past.   OSCAR

DOLLIE Were these flowers here?

PEGGY In the cold.

NORA All this is very old.

A few automobiles in the night.

—car doors being opened—
—crunching—
—badgers' cries—

fairly loud, as nine o'clock strikes, loud, even before
the strokes of eight o'clock have ended

> *—automobiles in snow—*
> *—police sirens—*
> *—turnstiles clicking—*

They have a Minnesota license   ANTHONY
plate.

I'm thirsty.   OSCAR

PEGGY In the night.

> *Striking the shaken rock, the water . . .*   READER

NORA I'm thirsty.

In the snow.   OSCAR

Descends in a fearful darkness . . .

> *—grunting—*
> *—sobs—*
> *—brass bands—*

not too loud, as ten o'clock strikes, fairly loud, even
before the strokes of nine o'clock have ended

—buzzing—
—car doors being opened—
—crunching—

I have a cousin in Minnesota.   BARBARA

PEGGY I'm thirsty.

> *Splashes back up in whirlwinds of foam to the*
> *east . . .*

A few couples looking for something to eat in the night.

NORA Hunger.

IVOR And suppose we go down to the tavern of the winds?

>   *Which rise above the trees, which fall like the smoke . . .*

NORA Farewell.

>   Well, it's a little late, I think.   JUDY

>   Hunger.   OSCAR

— mewing —
— icicles falling —
— train whistles —

fairly soft, as eleven o'clock strikes, not too loud, even before the strokes of ten o'clock have ended

>   *— cameras clicking —*
>   *— grunting —*
>   *— sobs —*

On the counters can be seen table napkins with waterfalls.

>   *With all the colors . . .*

PEGGY I'm hungry.

GINA I like it enormously, my pet, why are you nervous that way? I understand why you are nervous that way; I love you because you are nervous that way; you are a child, you could almost be my son, I have a son almost as big as you, but he is so ugly and silly . . . Only, in the midst of all this crowd and all this noise . . .

>   *That of a vast forest fire . . .*

>   I'm thirsty.   OSCAR

HELMUT Well, now you're the one who's jumpy!

PEGGY I'm cold.

>   *Then unrolls in a sheet of snow and glistens in the moonlight . . .*

Second Parenthesis of FEBRUARY

(The Challenge)

	In the past.	OSCAR

ANNOUNCER **On his tightrope, Jean-François Gravelet, called Blondin, cried out: "Does someone want to cross over on my back?"**

PEGGY Cross over on my back . . .

	Someone.	OSCAR

Alone

PEGGY In the past.

Harry Colcord, the impresario of Jean-François Gravelet, dared to take up the challenge.

	The mass of the river	READER
	Today.	OSCAR

which hurls itself

PEGGY In the night.

southward becomes rounded

	In the snow.	OSCAR

in a vast cylinder

PEGGY   Black.

In February the floodlight displays begin at 8:30 P.M.

over the chaos of the waves . . .

And the last iris of pure yellow gold.   ENOCH

In the black night.   OSCAR

Between the two falls juts out

Smoked yellow, plum red sepals   FELICIA
bordered in cream.

PEGGY   In the black snow.

*an island hollow underneath which hangs with all
its trees . . .*

Delicately perfumed.   ENOCH

In the past.   OSCAR

On very shapely stems.   FELICIA

PEGGY   In the black cold.

**Above the middle of the gorge, Jean-François Grave-
let, called Blondin, exhausted, asked Colcord to get
down; the latter had never set foot on a tightrope in
his life.**

All this is so old.   OSCAR

*The cataract divides into two branches and curves
into a horseshoe . . .*

PEGGY   In the black hunger.

In February the floodlight displays end at 11:00 P.M.

In the black thirst.   OSCAR

*Whose torrents rush toward the gaping mouth of
a chasm . . .*

PEGGY   In the black fear.

CLAUDIUS   I saw only you.

In the river.   OSCAR

It is less a river than a sea . . .

DOLLIE Were these flowers here?

PEGGY In this sea.

In this black.   OSCAR

Jean-François Gravelet, called Blondin, rested a few minutes, Colcord grasping at his thighs . . .

And at the edge of the cascade . . .

PEGGY In the past.

In the river.   OSCAR

PEGGY In the summer of the past.

In this sea.   OSCAR

The river runs on . . .

PEGGY In the winter in the midst of the summer of the past.

In this black.   OSCAR

From Lake Erie all the way to the cascade . . .

PEGGY In the snow in the midst of the sun of the past.

Harry Colcord succeeded in climbing again on the back of Jean-François Gravelet, called Blondin, and both were saved.

Their vertical height may be of about two hundred feet . . .

Floodlight displays.

—dance music—
—drops of water—
—crowds—

soft, as midnight strikes, fairly soft

—police whistles—
—mewing—
—icicles falling—

NNOUNCER   **A few automobiles in the night.**

Are the falls . . .   READER

PEGGY   Today the night.

In the thirst in the midst of the   OSCAR
hunger of today.

PEGGY   In the night in the midst of the bright day of the past.

They must have taken two days   ANTHONY
to get here.

In the fear in the midst of the   OSCAR
winter of today.

They have been married for two   BARBARA
days.

Third Parenthesis of FEBRUARY

(The Photograph)

IVOR Oh, you have the program, may I?

All this is so old.   OSCAR

ANNOUNCER **In a shop window can be seen the photograph of Anna Edson Taylor next to her barrel with her little cat.**

At about nine miles from the latter lake . . .   READER

PEGGY Who?

Why, of course.   JUDY

In the night glue.   OSCAR

GINA How could I be jumpy when I am near you, when I see you so fresh and so deliciously ill at ease. Then, you really want to go down with me into this tavern of the winds, it doesn't bore you too much to be in the company of a woman who is somewhat mature, who looks so much as if she were your mother?

And empties into the Ontario . . .

PEGGY Night ghoul.

Floodlight displays.

HELMUT Don't keep saying that all the time; you grate on my nerves.

Thorns.	ENOCH

Thorns. — ENOCH

Thirst in the cold. — OSCAR

Which springs from Lake Erie.

Red fruits. — FELICIA

PEGGY Fear in hunger.

One day a drop of blood on your mauve skin. — ENOCH

Snow in the black. — OSCAR

It is formed by the Niagara River . . .

One day a whole stained-glass window of savage blood in the yellowish white of your eyes of bronze. — FELICIA

Floodlight displays.

PEGGY In the tolling of the night.

CLAUDIUS Nor that elevator with its iron-and-glass cage on the other bank.

All this is so old. — OSCAR

On a counter can be seen postcards with waterfalls.

PEGGY   Night sleet.

ANNOUNCER   **A few automobiles in the night.**

— automobiles in snow —
— police sirens —
— turnstiles clicking —

very soft, as one o'clock strikes, soft

— panting —
— deep sighs —
— dance music —

Night peril.   OSCAR

A Wisconsin license.   ANTHONY

PEGGY   Night metal.

DOLLIE   Was that wax museum, "Madame Tussaud's," there?

Night faces.   OSCAR

Their saucepans are worn out.   BARBARA

PEGGY   Night tools.

An Illinois license.   ANTHONY

Night mud.   OSCAR

Their car covered with mud.   BARBARA

PEGGY   Night wax.

Fourth Parenthesis of FEBRUARY

(Wax Figures)

O all of you in your bedrooms en- KENNY
twined two by two.

ANNOUNCER **Dreams.**

Wax. OSCAR

Memories.

PEGGY Mud.

IVOR Well, then, perhaps we could go down as far as the
boat . . .

**In a shop window can be seen the photograph of Anna
Edson Taylor leaving her barrel, wounded, exhausted.**

Sleet, all this is so old, in the black OSCAR
tolling, in the hungry snow.

Well, it stops at twilight. JUDY

GINA I will be a good mother to you; you will never have had a
mother like me, you'll see. No, if you please, don't tell
me about your mother . . .

Cold in the thirst. OSCAR

HELMUT But you know very well that . . .

PEGGY   Night ghoul.

Floodlight displays.

                              In the night glue.   OSCAR

                              And the petals of your purplish   ENOCH
                              pink lips, velvety with black so per-
                              fumed, plucked by a ray of sunlight
                              in your bosses' basement.

PEGGY   Who?

                              All this is so old.   OSCAR

PEGGY   In the snow in the midst of the sun of the past.

                              The translucent red thorns sta-   FELICIA
                              tioned all along the cuttings you
                              planted at your bosses' place.

                              In the fear in the midst of the   OSCAR
                              bright day of the past.

PEGGY   In the night in the midst of the hunger of the winter of
today.

                              In the thirst of today, in this black   OSCAR
                              of winter in the midst of the sea of
                              the summer of the past, in this
                              river, this black . . .

XII

Coda

Track A: Omit the lines of Alfred, Beatrice, Clinton, Dolly, Elliott, Flora, Gaby, Herbert, Iannis, Janet and Kenneth.

Tracks B C: Omit the lines of Alfred, Beatrice, Clinton, Dolly, Elliott, Flora, Gaby and Herbert.

Tracks D E: Omit the lines of Alfred, Beatrice, Clinton, Dolly, Elliott, and Flora.

Tracks F G: Omit the lines of Alfred, Beatrice, Clinton, and Dolly.

Tracks H I: Omit the lines of Alfred and Beatrice.

Track J: Read everything.

CAST OF CHARACTERS

in the center:

loud:

READER

fairly loud:

at left: at right:

ANNOUNCER

IANNIS: vile   JANET: easy prey
seducer

not too loud:

GABY: old madam   LAURA: young woman alone

HERBERT: gigolo

QUENTIN: Frenchman, visiting professor at the University of Buffalo

fairly soft:

KENNETH: young man alone

ELLIOTT and FLORA: Negro
gardeners

soft:

CLINTON and DOLLY: old married couple

PATSY: Negro widow

very soft:

OMER: Negro   ALFRED and BEATRICE: "just-
widower   marrieds"

If the right-hand channel is closed, Janet can still be heard, but softly; Laura, but very softly; Elliott, Flora, Patsy, Alfred and Beatrice disappear.

If the left-hand channel is closed, Iannis can still be heard, but softly; Gaby, Herbert, Quentin, but very softly; Kenneth, Clinton, Dolly and Omer disappear.

Little Prelude for two o'clock in the morning.

After the first note of the Westminster carillon, soft, can be heard:

   in the center:

at left:

     at right:

   very soft:

not too loud:

     fairly soft:

  —date stamper—

    —car door being opened—

—leaf whispering—

    —buzzing—

—newsboy—

    —brass band—

—wind howling—

    —sob—

—curtain flapping—

    —grunting—

—kiss—

— camera clicking —

— birdcall —

— train whistle —

— splashing —

— icicle falling —

— eagle's cry —

— badger's cry —
— mewing —
— police whistle —

When one of the characters speaks, one of the sounds of the other side resumes its original volume.

When the Reader speaks, one of the left-hand sounds resumes its original volume, then one of the right-hand ones with the following line, and so in alternation.

When the Announcer speaks for the first time, one of the right-hand sounds resumes its original volume, the second time one of the left-hand ones, until the end.

There is a moment at which the sound covers the voice of the Announcer.

—cameras clicking—
—grunting—
—sobs—

soft, with the following notes of the carillon as two
o'clock strikes, very soft

> *—brass bands—*
> *—buzzing—*
> *—car doors being opened—*

> *We soon reached the edge·of the cataract,*   READER

ANNOUNCER   **The hour passes.**

> *which proclaimed its presence with frightful
> booming.*

QUENTIN   And I who am far from my living wife, separated from
her by the whole width of the Atlantic . . .

> *It is formed by the Niagara River*

> *—mewing—*
> *—badgers' cries—*
> *—icicles falling—*

fairly soft, as three o'clock strikes, soft, even before
the carillon has ended

—train whistles—
—cameras clicking—
—grunting—

Night passes.

> *which springs from Lake Erie*

OMER Farewell.

> *and empties into the Ontario.*

—winds howling—
—newsboys—
—leaves whispering—

not too loud, as four o'clock strikes, fairly soft, even before the carillon has ended

> *—police whistles—*
> *—mewing—*
> *—badgers' cries—*

The month passes.

> In the past.   PATSY

CLINTON That enormous tower that looks like a castle of water used not to be there.

> *Their vertical height is 144 feet.*

> A Missouri license plate.   ALFRED

DOLLY That little belfry with a carillon wasn't there.

> *—splashing—*
> *—birdcalls—*
> *—kisses—*

fairly loud, as five o'clock strikes, not too loud, and as the carillon ends

—curtains flapping—
—winds howling—
—newsboys—

> Fear.   PATSY

> They didn't want to take the time to   BEATRICE
> have it washed.

From Lake Erie all the way to the cascade, the river runs on

Hunger.   PATSY

Years pass.

along a steep incline,

Cold.   PATSY

What did I come looking for here?   LAURA

and at the edge of the falls,

Night.

— car doors being opened —
— date stampers —
— eagles' cries —

loud, as six o'clock strikes, fairly loud

> *— footsteps in snow —*
> *— splashing —*
> *— birdcalls —*

it is less a river than a sea

Thirst.   PATSY

KENNETH   O all of you chained naked flesh to naked flesh, night unto night . . .

whose torrents rush

The wind howling before dawn.

toward the gaping mouth

IANNIS   You saw the name of the boat . . .

Farewell.   PATSY

"The Virgin of the Mist."   JANET

of a chasm.

Dawn.

> *— grunting —*
> *— sobs —*
> *— brass bands —*

very loud, as seven o'clock strikes, loud

—buzzing—
—car doors being opened—
—date stampers—

> *The cataract divides into two branches,*

The quarrels of the dawn.

> *and curves*

GABY   When I came here with my husband.

> *into a horseshoe. Between the two falls*

Daybreak.

—badgers' cries—
—icicles falling—
—train whistles—

loud, as eight o'clock strikes, very loud

> *—cameras clicking—*
> *—grunting—*
> *—sobs—*

> *juts out*

> Your fingernails painted like petals   ELLIOTT
> fallen to earth.

> *an island hollow underneath which hangs with all
> its trees*

Morning.

> *over the chaos of the waves.*

CLINTON   The bridge collapsed five years later.

HERBERT   Because you came here with your husband?

DOLLY   After thirty years we have come back.

> *The mass of the river which hurls itself southward*

> *—newsboys—*
> *—leaves rustling—*
> *—police whistles—*

fairly loud, as nine o'clock strikes, loud

— mewing —
— badgers' cries —
— icicles falling —

The cities.

An Arizona license.   ALFRED

Your hands covered with earth,   FLORA
which you washed in order to caress
me, but which still smelled of soap
and earth with the scent of roses
over the manure, and your nails
still all framed in earth like young
sprouts.

becomes rounded in a vast cylinder

— birdcalls —
— kisses —
— curtains flapping —

not too loud, as ten o'clock strikes, fairly loud, even
before the strokes of nine o'clock have ended

— winds howling —
— newsboys —
— leaves rustling —

Two or three nights.   BEATRICE

then unrolls in a sheet of snow

Thaw.

— date stampers —
— eagles' cries —
— footsteps in snow —

fairly soft, as eleven o'clock strikes, not too loud, even
before the strokes of ten o'clock have ended

— splashing —
— bird calls —
— kisses —

and glistens

What is it that draws me here   LAURA
anyway?

in the sun with all the colors.

Water.

*The one falling to the east descends in a fearful
darkness,*

KENNETH   Behind all these black panes arousing vice or love . . .

one would say a pillar of water from the flood.

—*sobs*—
—*brass bands*—
—*buzzing*—

soft, as noon strikes, fairly soft, even before the
strokes of eleven o'clock have ended

—*car doors being opened*—
—*date stampers*—
—*eagles' cries*—

Mud.

A thousand rainbows

IANNIS   You can't read. It isn't "The Virgin"; it's "The Be-
trothed of the Mist," or "The Lover."

curve and cross over the abyss.

The crowd.

Striking the shaken rock,

GABY   I had begged him, I was very young then, I knew nothing about his life, I was younger even than you are now,
and I was beautiful then, I was very beautiful, you can't
imagine.

the water splashes back up in whirlwinds of foam

CLINTON   After the flood.

Hail, my bronze leaves whom I   ELLIOTT
have so watched over.

which rise

Their green blood on your rough FLORA
fingers.

above the trees

My buds of milky coral. ELLIOTT

—icicles falling—
—train whistles—
—cameras clicking—

very soft, as one o'clock strikes, soft

—grunting—
—sobs—
—brass band—

like the smoke

Kisses.

of a vast forest fire.

Sparkling eyes.

Do you know why? JANET

DOLLY It was before the war.

Pines, wild walnut trees, rocks cut into phantom
forms

CLINTON It was a steel bridge.

HERBERT You know very well.

And the bees buzzing in their FLORA
tea bush in the midst of walls of
skin.

A Kentucky license plate. ALFRED

DOLLY It is a concrete bridge.

adorn the scene.

Do you think, say, do you think BEATRICE
. . .

Eagles

CLINTON Everything has changed.

swept along

What were you saying?   ALFRED

by the current.

Tears.

of air

DOLLY   We have changed.

descend

Me?   BEATRICE

in spirals

Blood.

to the depths of the chasm.

Of course, you.   ALFRED

I said something?   BEATRICE

I thought so.   ALFRED

I don't remember.   BEATRICE

*And badgers hang by their flexible tails at the end
of a low branch to catch in the abyss the broken
carcasses of the elks and of the bears.*

**This is the description of the falls that François-René
de Chateaubriand published on April 2, 1801, in
his novel, "Atala, or The Love of Two Savages in the
Wilderness."**